CW01032908

THE FI
BOAT BOOK

To the boat designers
who brought cement boatbuilding
into the seventies.

The First Ferro Boat Book

PETE GREENFIELD

HOLLIS & CARTER
LONDON SYDNEY
TORONTO

British Library Cataloguing
in Publication Data
Greenfield, Pete
The first ferro boat book.
1. Concrete boats—Design and construction
I. Title
623.82'07'33   VM323
ISBN 0–370–30066–1
0–370–30090–4 Pbk

© Pete Greenfield 1978
Printed in Great Britain for
Hollis & Carter
an associate company of
The Bodley Head Ltd
9 Bow Street, London WC2E 7AL
by Cox & Wyman Ltd,
London, Fakenham and Reading
Set in Monophoto Baskerville
First published 1978

This book is sold subject to the condition that
it shall not, by way of trade or otherwise, be
lent, re-sold, hired out, or otherwise circu-
lated without the publisher's prior consent in
any form of binding or cover other than that
in which it is published and without a similar
condition including this condition being
imposed on the subsequent purchaser.

CONTENTS

CONTENTS

List of Photographs

The photographs were all supplied by the author, with the following exceptions:
1, by courtesy of Roy Montgomery and Jay R. Benford & Assoc. Inc.; 40, by courtesy of Jay R. Benford & Assoc. Inc.; 2, 6, 7 and 12, by courtesy of Richard Hartley; 16, 17, 21, 23–5, 28, 30–2, 39, 43 and 44, by courtesy of Brian Williamson; 45, by courtesy of Mike Robson.

The line illustrations were all supplied by Brian Hancock, with the following exceptions:
3, by courtesy of New Zealand Ferro Services; 4, by courtesy of Robert Tucker; 5, 22 and 23, by courtesy of Percy Dalton; 6, by courtesy of Ferro-cement Marine Services; 7, 8, 9 and 21, by courtesy of Jay R. Benford & Assoc. Inc.

INTRODUCTION

There have been several books already on the subject of ferrocement boatbuilding: this is patently *not* the first one.

As an amateur boatbuilder, I found that I had to do considerable reading—and ask a lot of patient ferrocement boatbuilders a lot of questions—before I knew what were the basic alternative methods open to me if I chose to build in ferrocement. I wanted to know which options I had to choose from, but all I seemed to read was history. The more practical books, when I found them, confused me by conflicting markedly with each other: now, with a little experience, these different viewpoints are stimulating, but at the beginning they were a worry. Another worry was that these books were written by professional designers with years of experience: did they really know just how green and ham-fisted I was?

Hopefully then, this fills a need as a first book to read on the building of a ferrocement boat: a book to introduce some of the alternative methods and how beginners coped with them, and a book to encourage you to read further and with more understanding. So that it is of more continued usefulness, there are some suggestions for first ferro boatbuilding projects and details of the ways that we and other amateurs coped with the difficulties we encountered.

Throughout this book, you will find the names of amateur boatbuilders, professional boat designers and many others, all too numerous to list individually here, who have given so much help in so many ways that, again, listing every single contribution would be impossible. So many and so much that on sleepless nights, I'll worry that I might have inadvertently misrepresented one or more. Thus, with a hope that any clangers are forgivable ones, my sincere and very grateful thanks to them all.

Special thanks must also go to Denny Desoutter, editor of 'Practical Boat Owner' magazine, who has not only allowed me to use some material originally printed there but actually volunteered for the unenviable task of editing all of this. Similarly to David Brenchley of Cornish Photo-News, for making real photographs from my diabolical negatives; to Brian Hancock, for making real diagrams from my apparently drunken doodles and to Percy Dalton for more than just his delightful drawings. Also for much unobtrusive kindness, not least in saving us from homelessness during the book's writing, we owe a great deal to Ray Allerton of Penryn Bridge Boatyard.

And as ever, the most special thanks of all to Maggie, for everything.

Pete Greenfield,
Simplicity, Penryn, 1977

I

Ferro tales . . . and you

FERROCEMENT BOATBUILDING IS FUN! FUN! FUN! In fact, it's a doddle. Your granny could do it. All she would have to do is get hold of some boat-shaped rods, wrap a few rolls of wire-netting around them, spend a lazy day watching plasterers splashing mortar about and she would have a boat to cross oceans. Perhaps you also believe that Ghengis Khan was the first liberal democrat, St Michael is the patron saint of underpants, there really is a Santa Claus (Virginia) and it isn't just in London North-West-One that you find fairies at the bottom of the garden. For if you believe such tales about ferrocement boatbuilding, maybe you'll believe anything.

Maybe people still start a cement boat believing that here, at last, is the ultimate boatbuilding material—dirt cheap, idiot-proof and everlasting. Defects, none. Weaknesses, none. Difficulties, none. Maybe they start out thinking that way but I'll bet you if they finish the boat, somewhere along the line, probably quite soon, they modify that view more than a little. I do not believe that St Peter spends his half-day off from the gate doing a spot of celestial long-lining from a ferrocement fishing smack. The perfect boatbuilding material may well exist up there but I doubt that it's ferrocement.

Down here, along with wood, steel, resinglass and the rest, ferrocement is just another imperfect way of building boats. It's true that you can get by without the skills needed to build boats in wood or steel but what you do not need in skills, you must have in patience and perseverance if you choose ferrocement. You do not need the controlled environment which is essential to build well using resins; you can build a ferro boat in the open air. But in Britain that means you spend half the year in mud to the top of your boots, with one wire-twisting hand warm while the rest of you is cold—and wet—from the incessant dripping of rusty rainwater. And the winters are worse.

Have I put you off yet? What, the cost? You reckon it must be cheap or why would anyone use it. Well, maybe, once upon a time it was but have you seen the price of a roll of wire mesh lately and—this is important—the price of epoxy fillers and fancy paints? You have probably read elsewhere that the cost of any bare hull is but a fraction of the cost of a finished boat—some say less than a quarter. Unless you are building a coal barge, you have still got to fit the thing out and yacht chandlers charge like the Light Brigade.

But it is durable, you're saying, you've got to admit that it's durable. Yes, I have got to admit, it is durable. Apart, that is, from the cracks. I've yet to see a ferro boat without a crack or two somewhere. But they never go deeper than the first layer of netting and they have the strange property of healing themselves in time so I suppose yes, it is durable. There are, of course, the bare rusting wires. If your plastering team is going to lay a really thin skin of mortar over the mesh (which they absolutely must), then there are bound to be a few wires left exposed somewhere and they will rust. Sure, you can chip them out, stop up with epoxy filler and paint over; but for durable, don't read maintenance-free, not for the first few years. Just durable. Apart that is, from the possible dangers of electrolytic action. Well, you were going to use galvanized mesh, weren't you? . . . and you know what galvanizing is? Zinc, that's right. And what do they use for sacrificial anodes? Zinc, right again. Certainly, you do not have to use the bronze skin fittings and copper-based anti-fouling that complete a cell which can eat away the boat faster than you can chip away and insulate with epoxy. So I suppose, yes, you're right, it's durable.

Is this becoming too depressing? Perhaps you have already given up the idea of ever building anything in ferrocement in favour of beating yourself with a bramble branch because it sounds as much fun and the exercise would be more beneficial. Maybe I have made an over-determined effort to dispel the daydreams encouraged by firms selling boat plans and escapism to innocents with no boating experience at all. It is my belief that even the knowledgeable beginner—the one who knows that all boats cost time and money and effort—should steel himself against the seduction of dream-ship advertising. To learn the real advantages of ferrocement (yes, it does have some), it is not enough to read one advert, one article in a boating magazine or one book (even this one!). In fact, there is a much better way of learning the truth than any reading.

If at all possible, you must go out and see real-life cement boats, both built and building. Keep asking boating friends till you locate your first amateur builder; he will direct you to the rest. Bear in mind, though, that most amateur builders will welcome you like a vampire being visited by the vicar. After all, if they are building in their spare time, they will have no time to spare to advise you. So be thoughtful. Stop by briefly the first couple of times: let the builder know that yours is more than a passing interest and try to discover when he has his tea-break or knocks off for the day: the best time to engage him in conversation.

Ignore his first monosyllabic grunts—he gets a lot of time-wasters—and suffuse your first questions with an intelligent appreciation of his achievement and dumb hero worship in equal measure. Don't assume his wife is simply there to hold the welding rods prettily; odds on she knows more about ferrocement boatbuilding than you do. Treat her like the boatbuilders' Anna Raeburn and she may be the first to give you some real advice. Somehow men boatbuilders are harder to reach at first but if you avoid being funny—he's heard your original quips three times this week already—and mention other local ferro projects, implying that his is superior but you are not sure why, he will see that your perceptions are sound and may well explain where the others went wrong— in some detail. You might also mention books you have read but please, not this one—I've got enough problems! Finally —perhaps after tying wires or rubbing down cement— choose your moment and ask him why he chose ferrocement. Wait patiently; it isn't an easy question to answer well surrounded by mud, rust and mesh; he may well have forgotten himself.

While the poor guy is mulling it over, perhaps it would be only fair if I also made the effort to explain why we chose ferro. Perhaps the single most important reason for us was that specific skills are not needed to build in ferrocement. Though I had built one and a half dinghies (that's another story), I lacked the confidence to build a large boat in wood. My welding expertise was worse, being nil. My only real asset was my wife Maggie who not only shared my enthusiasm for our boatbuilding project but also most definitely did not want to be relegated to the role of a tea-making decoration or, as she put it, playing Piglet to my Pooh. We both wanted the boat to be a shared venture and ferrocement put us on level footing. What is more, within the parameters of our limited abilities, ferrocement seemed to offer us the best chance of achieving a strong and watertight ship. We could imagine the strength of six or more layers of mesh embedded in concrete and formed into one homogenous curved shape, long before we read any of the facts and figures. Just as important was that, unlike many other boatbuilding methods, with ferrocement there are no long seams to be made leakproof.

But it was not just lack of confidence in our abilities that ruled out wood, as any amateur boatman will have guessed.

The prodigious prices of boat timber (or, come to that, steel plate or resins) mean that the wise way to buy is in bulk, perhaps obtaining a large discount by buying all the basic materials for the whole boat in one go. You need, therefore, not only confidence but a healthy lump sum available at the start. We had neither so we chose ferro. The outlay required for the steel to build the frames and stringers is not that great. Thus one can build the skeleton of the craft reasonably cheaply and then stand back and 'see' the finished boat, judging her shape and your workmanship before you have sunk too much money into the project; thereafter, if you decide to continue, all you need is patience and plasterers. Another advantage—available then but alas no longer—was that mesh was cheap enough to be bought by the roll as we could afford it. Since then prices have risen so much that the advantages of piecemeal purchasing look much less attractive against the chance of up to 33 per cent discount for the buyer who shops around with a large order.

The author of one of the most sensible ferro books, Jay R. Benford, advocates building the boat indoors and, doubtless, there are considerable advantages in doing so but for Mag and me, as with many others, the choice was never available. We could not find any building to hire in which to build a boat twenty feet long, let alone big enough for the thirty-footer we wanted. It was outside or nothing. Fortunately, of all the boatbuilding materials, the steel in a ferrocement boat suffers least from exposure to the elements since some rusting etches the surface of the metal for better cement adhesion. As long as large flaking areas of rust are brushed clean before plastering, the boat basket can easily withstand any amount of weather for a year or two—I wish I could say the same for ferro boatbuilders!

Our final argument in favour was specifically related to our choice of design. I suppose it's a sort of inverted snobbery but most yachts—especially 'yachty' yachts—leave me yawning.

1 Jay R. Benford's 20-foot 'Gaff Sloop' *Ragnar*, wired and plastered
at the 1972 Seattle Boatshow.

It isn't just that they are the pampered plastic perks of the
privileged (which they are . . . er . . . brothers), it is because
the uniformity of stainless steel and resinglass seems to have
infected the designers' abilities to draw bold, fresh shapes.
Maybe they are all drawn by computers anyway and computers can't draw sexy curves. For me, the real boats—boats
with individuality and character (and sexy curves!)—are the
old working boats. Since I grew up at the grotty end of the

Humber where grandad had been a lighterman and dad piloted little coasters, perhaps all I've done is combine an early conditioning with a liking for sail. Whatever the cause, I wanted an old-style workboat, more barge than yacht.

Of course, restoring a full-size barge is a rich man's pastime these days and scaling down line drawings never works well. However, looking at photographs of old barges, I was reminded by those bluff bows and hard bilges of another more famous 'barge': Joshua Slocum's *Spray*. To build *Spray* as she was built—with massive timbers, 2-inch planking, 6 by 6 beams and the like—would cost the earth these days. With ferrocement, however, we could build heavily and, relatively, cheaply. Like many others, we found that in recreating the displacement craft of the last century, the potential weight of ferrocement is a positive advantage.

These then are the empirical and personal reasons which prompted us to choose ferrocement. I don't doubt that your chap's answer will involve totally different virtues. You'll need the question answered several times before you can begin to see which of ferro's advantages are relevant to you personally. If you want technical evaluations, tables of weights, compressive strengths and elasticity, this book will help you less than others, but once you have heard what amateurs have had to say, you may well wish to broaden your knowledge with further reading. Of course, you don't have to buy every book: some are of real practical usefulness as tools and others are merely background reading. As I have said before, many books will contradict each other but the more you read, the less chance there is of building the wrong design the wrong way. Let's look at what's available.

There are possibly three generations of textbooks on ferro boatbuilding. Those of the first were concerned to convince doubtful conservatives that here was a genuine boatbuilding method, worthy of comparison with the more established materials. The earliest of these books sometimes express

views of quite antique quaintness, so it is well worth a look
to see when a book was last revised. However, from any book
of this generation you will learn lots about the provenance
of ferrocement, considerably less about designs for the
material and next to nothing about techniques.

The second generation of books are much more practical
in their approach since these books are written by designers
of stock plans for amateur building. Thus the books are not
only manuals on construction techniques, they are also design
catalogues. In theory, of course, if you are building a stock
plan by Designer A, his textbook should be all you need.
However, it is possible that you may want to vary that plan
just a little or maybe Designer A is one of those who has not
written his own textbook or maybe he has and you can't
understand it. Since the chances are that he lives several
thousand miles away, you consult the book by Designer B
instead. That is when your troubles start, for not only will
Designer B advocate entirely different ferrocement techniques, he will tell you—with careful regard to the laws of
libel—that if Designer A designed a rubber duck, it would
sink. Of course, if you consult him, Designer C will say both
the others are at sea, see? All of which leaves the inexperi-
enced amateur sorely in need of down-to-earth and totally
impartial appraisals of the various techniques recommended
by different designers.

The combination of careful explanation and those impartial appraisals should come from the literature of generation three. Already, it ranges from the learned, sometimes
'heavy' reports in the Journal of the New Zealand Ferrocement Association and investigations by the United Nations
Food & Agriculture Organization and various fishing
authorities, into ferrocement fishing craft, and to 'grass roots'
reports in the boating magazines of the actual experiences of
amateur boatbuilders. Hopefully this book will have a place
among such reports for I shall try to describe how we and

2 Richard Hartley's 'RORC 32' *Moonbird*, built by Dennis Bailey in eighteen months, with the rig she used from New Zealand to Fiji.

other amateurs like us built a ferrocement boat. None of us is qualified to give expert opinions, but I can pass on to you disinterested assessments of the methods we all used: which worked, which didn't, and which were most difficult in the doing. When you have read of our efforts, I do not think you will still believe that 'Ferro is Fun'—if you ever did—but you may sense that it can be an alternative way of building a boat

19

with its own satisfactions. Whether you too would find it satisfying depends more on you than the nature of ferrocement.

I wonder just what motives prompted you to pick up this book and read it this far or rather, just why you want to build a boat? It's my belief that the seeds of failure of any boatbuilding project by amateurs are firmly rooted among the blossoming plans that started it all. Maybe the amateur can build a dinghy without spending too much time and money or even mental involvement on the project but you don't build dinghies in ferrocement—yet. Ferrocement boats take time—great wedges of it: days, weekends, months, years. If you start your boat in a tearing hurry to get away from it all and you are counting the hours from the start, that's a seed of potential failure. Ideally, I suppose, the ferro boatbuilder should start with time on his hands and nothing —certainly no other person—to cause problems through neglect.

In Appendix A, where I have tried to present several detailed pictures of ferro boatbuilding projects, I have made a point of noting the time taken by each builder. Only one cement boat I know was built in weeks and that was by Stan Goldman: though he is not a boatbuilder, Stan is a skilled engineer and the boat is 22 feet long. It took Sonny and Kathy Wieck, amateurs starting with a frame kit, four years to build their pretty little 18-footer. Maybe both examples are extremes: certainly I know of no boat over thirty feet which was amateur built in less than two years. Please think on it. Every ferro builder I know has been visited by some potential builder who is always, always, always going to build his boat faster. They never do.

Money itself—or the lack of it—rarely seems to stop a project though it often slows it down. Most builders seem to collect boat gear and timber from the start, so there is always something to be renovated or made up while waiting to afford mesh or mortar. Sometimes a failure is attributed to lack of money when lack of forethought is the cause. It is lack of forethought when you build a hull so large that you cannot afford to fit her out. I know that once upon a time boatbuilding books told you to build the biggest boat you could afford. That was before they invented inflation, sailor! My advice would be to work out the size boat you can just build comfortably within your means—and then choose a design six feet shorter. Believe me, with the costs of steel and cement soaring like Concorde and the astronomical prices of the little things—a handful of screws, a couple of bolts, a masonry bit—by the time you have finished that smaller boat, she *will* be the biggest you can afford!

As to the draining of your mental energy, which such a project is capable of, you fare better if you have some abilities you need not worry over. Maybe you do not need special skills to work with ferrocement but if you are building a boat, it helps if you are a boatbuilder. Oh yes, an amateur certainly, with none of the pro's experience or skills but the sooner you start to acquire even the smallest fraction of that experience, just one of those skills, the less of a worry and risk your boat will be. Save lots of cynical commonsense for the claims of those who sell the plans of large yachts which can be built 'without any previous boatbuilding experience'. Maybe they can but I am sure that they can be built one hell of a lot quicker and cheaper without the time-wasting and expensive mistakes caused by total inexperience and with a lot fewer sleepless nights into the bargain.

Any large boat will need a tender. If you have no boatbuilding experience at all, build a little dinghy first, maybe with second-hand timber and building ply: it will still last a few years and your mistakes will be cheap ones. Even an eight-foot praam has lines and offsets, frames and stringers; all things you'll come up against in your larger ferro craft. Don't forget also that when your cementing is complete, you will still have a boat to furnish, inevitably in wood. If you build a cement hull only to be stymied at the first bulkhead, hatch or bunk-frame, the failure you leave behind will be yet another eyesore on the ecology—'Ferro Hull (Conspic.)' on your local harbour chart. I can understand anyone anxious to get started on a dreamship but while you are still at the stage of looking at the other fellows' boats, of reading the other fellows' books— and re-designing that dreamship with every boat and book you come across—building a little dinghy is something practical and useful to be getting on with. Go on, start making sawdust and shavings as your first real step in ferrocement boatbuilding, while you re-design your dreamship yet again.

2

'Beyond a wholesome discipline, be gentle with yourself'

Desiderata, an anonymous homily, 1692

I suppose all ships must start as dreams but the sooner you get down to serious planning, the sooner you'll sail her. Trouble is, you can think that you are planning very seriously when really you are still dreaming. Don't imagine that this boat—or any other—can be everything you have always wanted: dreamboats might be all things at all times but real boats are compromises.

Eventually you have to define her function: is she to be a dayboat, a cruising boat (sail, power or both), a fishing boat, houseboat, etc.? You'll notice that light displacement craft are not included in that list: you know, fast powerboats, racing yachts and the like. Not because such things are impossible in ferrocement—more than one concrete boat has won races— but because, as boats for a first project, they present extra difficulties of building down to rather precise weight limits. If you must have a racer, may I suggest you build a very small conventional ferro hull beforehand to gain experience (Jay Benford has plans for a delightful 14ft 'tugboat', for example), or choose another boatbuilding material from the outset. It's a mistake to demand too much from yourself first time around: as long as she looks nice and gets you places, your first ferro boat ought to be as easy to build as you can make her.

However, having encouraged you to choose a conventionally 'heavy' ferrocement boat design, it must be said right now that there are more ways than one of building ferro boats. There are heavy cement boats and heavy cement boats . . . and some are a lot lighter than others. Many modern ferrocement designs feature much thinner—and therefore lighter—hull skins than the designs of ten to fifteen years ago. I'll try to list the various basic combinations of mesh and steel that have been tried so far.

The Good Old-Fashioned Way

This is the method your granny would choose: Richard Hartley calls it the 'hollow log' method and it's the one that most newcomers to ferrocement have heard about. As Hartley implies, it is responsible for giving a bad name to smaller ferrocement boats.

What happens is that black steel waterpipe or steam pipe— usually about an inch outside diameter—is bent up into stem, keel and transom and into a large number of frames and the whole lot are welded together to form the boat's skeleton. Sometimes this boat-shaped framework is set up on vacant ground with everything supported by strategically sited timbers; more often the builder erects a 'cage' to support and locate the boat's backbone and frames. The next step is to fasten fore and aft steel rods to the water-pipe ribs. These stringers—as they are called—may be parallel to the keel, the waterline or the sheerline or a bit of all three. The rod used can be mild steel, Hard Drawn (more springy) or High Tensile (springier still): whichever, it is usually around $\frac{1}{4}$ inch in diameter and the rods are laid at 2-inch spacings. Fastening the rod to the pipe-frames is accomplished by welding if mild steel is used, but the other two types require wire tying since the process which makes them springy also makes them hard to weld—thus you deduce correctly that H.T. is harder to weld than H.D. The old way often demands a second layer of stringers before any mesh is applied. These run vertically from keel to sheer, usually inside the fore and aft stringers. Their spacing depends on the closeness of the pipe-frames but

6 inches is not untypical. These verticals can be the same diameter as the other stringers or somewhat smaller and are always tied, never welded in place.

With the basketry complete, the builder begins to attach the chicken wire netting that, again, I am sure you have heard about. Size and number of layers can vary. Originally, 1-inch netting was commonly used but later $\frac{1}{2}$-inch 22-gauge hexagonal galvanized netting became favourite. In Britain such netting comes in 50-metre rolls, 36 inches wide (such is metrication!) and builders generally apply the mesh to the hull in vertical strakes, one layer at a time. On a 40-footer, there might be 8 layers of mesh: 4 inside the rods and 4 out. Initial tying to hold the mesh to the rod framework is done with steel wire, probably between 1 and 2 mm in diameter— a short length goes through the mesh, round a rod and back to be twisted tight with pliers. When all eight layers have been tacked in position in this manner, more intensive tying with the same wire follows to pull all layers into as tight a sandwich as possible: a 2-inch spacing in any direction is not uncommon. With the protruding twists of wire bent back into the mesh, the hull is then ready for plastering and curing and these processes need a chapter of their own.

That, then, is the way that the steelwork for most cement boats was constructed until well into the sixties. It is still possible to see large ferrocement boats being built this way today —the additional weight being a positive advantage in that it saves ballast costs. However, on boats of 40 feet and under, it is more likely that some variations of the technique I have described are being used. These may simply be variations of scantlings (dimensions of components) or more radical differences. Before I describe some of these differences, let me mention why they exist: in other words, what's wrong with doing it the good old-fashioned way?

There are two basic faults and the most limiting of the two is excessive weight. Two layers of $\frac{1}{4}$-inch rods and eight layers of chicken netting produce a hull thickness of over an inch when cemented in the usual way, and that means a weight per square foot of over 15 lb. In other words, this type of ferrocement construction is just too heavy for designing boats much under forty feet long, unless considerable sacrifices are made in the other aspects of design. The second fault is that often these boats just do not look very good: instead of fair curves, the most uncritical of owners saw a 'starved dog' look with hollows between the frames, or perhaps a more general 'sack of potatoes' appearance with lumps and bumps everywhere.

As a result, when today's amateur builders adopt a different approach to ferrocement boatbuilding from the old-fashioned way, it is usually with the aim of reducing weight or improving appearance—or both. Many now use the specific techniques advocated by the American designer Jay R. Benford or those of New Zealander Richard Hartley or, like myself and others, they may select a mixture of methods from both schools of thought and some others to suit their own needs and skills. Both Jay Benford and Richard Hartley have their own eminently sensible and practical manuals on how their boats should be built, which include lots of useful advice for people building boats by other designers. However, to give you a rough idea of the progress of ferrocement from the days of the lumpy heavyweights, I'll try to précis their two techniques.

Jay Benford's Approach

Jay Benford continues to advocate waterpipe frames, when closely spaced, but not exclusively. He also suggests the use of rod frames and these are sometimes tied to timber moulds to ensure that they maintain their shape. When the cement is dry, the timber moulds are removed and the exposed rod frame is plastered over. An alternative form of framing is employed where bulkheads occur. These are web frames (also called truss frames) made from two parallel mild steel rods held apart by a third zig-zag rod tack-welded to the other two.

However, in his choice of mesh, Jay Benford is much more definitive. He recommends the exclusive use of non-galvanized $\frac{1}{2}$-inch square welded mesh. The combination of the larger wire section and the welded squares means that this mesh is much stiffer to handle than the softer chicken wire and weighs nearly twice as much per square foot. It comes in 30-metre rolls in Britain where, unfortunately, it is obtainable only in galvanized form. Such a roll of welded mesh costs

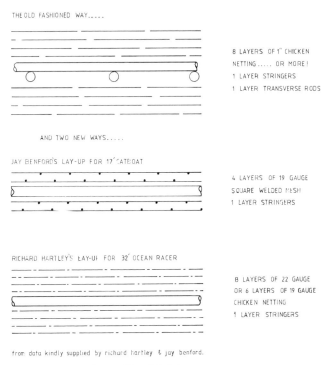

THE OLD FASHIONED WAY.....

8 LAYERS OF 1" CHICKEN
NETTING ..... OR MORE!
1 LAYER STRINGERS
1 LAYER TRANSVERSE RODS

AND TWO NEW WAYS.....

JAY BENFORD'S LAY-UP FOR 17' CATBOAT

4 LAYERS OF 19 GAUGE
SQUARE WELDED MESH
1 LAYER STRINGERS

RICHARD HARTLEY'S LAY-UP FOR 32' OCEAN RACER

8 LAYERS OF 22 GAUGE
OR 6 LAYERS OF 19 GAUGE
CHICKEN NETTING
1 LAYER STRINGERS

from data kindly supplied by richard hartley & jay benford.

Fig 1 Mesh lay-ups.

nearly the same as a 50-metre roll of chicken netting, but because of increased strength and steel density Mr Benford recommends only three layers of welded mesh inside and out for the sort of hull size that would require eight layers of chicken wire in all, making mesh costs roughly comparable. He also recommends that the three layers of mesh are tied together before being applied to the boat horizontally in boat-length strakes. Details of just how this is done are given in his *Practical Ferrocement Boatbuilding*.

The Benford way is to apply the inner mesh to the frames, tie it temporarily in place and then weld mild steel stringers in the conventional position, welding through the mat of mesh. The increased rigidity of a welded mesh hull means that vertical stringers of small diameter H.T. rod are needed only for quite large designs: on smaller boats the outer mesh is applied to one layer of stringers only. By omitting this second layer, compacting the welded mesh and scraping and brushing the inside of the hull on plastering day, Jay Benford can offer considerable advances over that old-style ferro-cement forty-footer. Using welded mesh, he not only achieves a fairer hull but the complementary weight-saving means that he can offer plans for a ferro boat only twelve feet long!

Richard Hartley's Boats . . .

. . . start bigger, at around 27 feet overall, but he too has managed to overcome the bugbear of heavy hulls, often in distinctively modern designs. Mr Hartley banishes the old waterpipe frames, saying that not only do they produce un-sightly bulges inside the boat, they also provide insufficient support to keep the hull in shape during building and plaster-ing. Instead he uses web frames made from mild steel rod throughout the boat. Each frame has a moulded depth of only three inches and the centre zig-zag is replaced by a number of short stirrups. I can attest personally that these frames are plenty strong enough to bear the weight of workers throughout the building process and a further advantage of this type of frame is that it removes the worry of what might be deteriorating inside poorly filled waterpipes.

High tensile stringers are used on Hartley designs, a second layer of thinner diagonal stringers being required only on designs over forty feet. The hull basket is then finished off with six or eight layers of $\frac{1}{2}$-inch chicken netting and wire tying is conventional. With these construction methods, Richard Hartley can save so much weight that he is able to offer such features as ferrocement decks, and even coachroofs, on his smallest designs.

So what both designers have done is to keep—and improve on—the strength of the old-fashioned hull structure and yet find ways of reducing weights: Benford using welded mesh, Hartley using web frames. I am sure that you will have already guessed that many amateurs today combine the two systems by using welded mesh and web frames throughout. Of course, there are other permutations possible as well bringing in new ideas like removable web frames, shadow moulds, etc. You may also hear of glass-reinforced cement, ferro-resin (the ferro basket is 'plastered' with a filler made from polyester resin and sawdust), 'Fer-a-lite', stapling mesh to a timber plug, and so on. All of these ideas are well worth considering, especially if you can find someone able to share with you direct experience of them: I am sure that if the system has been proved to be a good one, word will have spread and you will come across someone who has used it successfully.

Just one example of these alternative methods, for instance, is the system Maggie and I employed of hanging the hull basket inside a scaffolding cage rather than working upward from a supported keel as many ferro boats and most wooden ones are built. It was not a way we had read much about but one we found other amateurs using and their boats seemed particularly fair. They said—and we later discovered it to be true—that in return for a little more steel and effort at the setting-up stage, you get much easier alignment of the frames and trouble-free meshing and plastering of the keel. It probably only works where web frames are used as they rigidly maintain the hull shape, and those gifted at setting up boat frames 'by guess and by God' will surely consider it extra, unnecessary effort, but for us it seemed worthwhile— and it worked.

Whichever method seems most attractive to you at this stage, I suggest you leave the question pending while you read further. I know that many amateurs tend to shy away from web frames, for instance, in the belief that pipe bending must be easier for those with absolutely no experience of welding. Perhaps quite a few pipe frame boats get started for just that reason. However, as you read on, you'll discover that many amateurs who had never welded anything in their lives have made successful web frame boats . . . and that even pipe frame boats mean welding! I urge you to postpone any decisions about construction until you have made your decisions on design.

You may have already come across ferrocement literature that lists points of design to look for in a concrete boat; if not, you will. I would bear such pointers in mind but I would not let them put you off a shape you have set your heart on. Designers these days seem able to reproduce most of the features of the conventional displacement hull in ferrocement as long as they are allowed to incorporate internal reinforcing webs as necessary. However, while that's so, there are still some design features which, while certainly possible, do provide more difficulties for the builder. In other words, some shapes are far less of a bother in the building than others.

Working from the keel up, the keel itself is the first consideration. Timber hulls, even large ones, tend to have relatively narrow keels and deadwoods and if such features are copied in a cement boat, problems may arrive at the meshing stage. Most amateurs like to make the keel and much of the deadwood hollow so that ballast can be added later, perhaps even when the boat is afloat. This means that the interior of these boxes must be covered with mesh and wire-tied, which can be a problem if such areas are too narrow to be got at, particularly if she is a deep-keeler. On very small boats, you just have to manage somehow, but on boats large enough to take it, it is a considerable help if the designer has increased the keel width to 9 inches to a foot. Of course, a wider keel also helps to concentrate the weight of the ballast as low as possible, if that is your aim.

3 The web-type sternpost on Luc Delahaie's 38-foot double-ender.

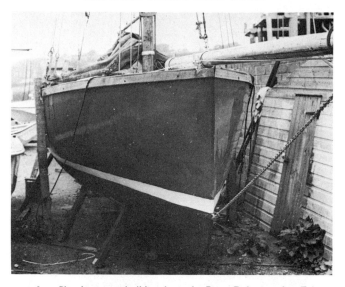

4 & 5 Simple easy-to-build ends on the Percy Dalton 22-foot Falmouth working boat design.

I am sure that you can see without much elaboration on my part that the traditional type of long straight keel saves a deal of lofting and steel bending, and is also considerably easier to set up in its correct position in relation to the frames, stem and sternpost. Fin keelers may be more trendy but they require more measuring, bending and still more measuring in the setting up. The stem shape deserves some consideration for the same reasons. If you can love the old Victorian plumb stem then the only bend will be in the forefoot: most can't, so must work harder to shape up a curved stem. Most work of all comes in those frequent ferro designs that feature a reverse curve clipper bow, the knuckle of the forefoot and yet another reverse curve into the keel.

It is not a feature of hull shape but, while we are up forward, do take note where the designer puts frame number

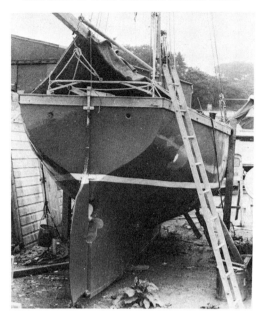

one if she is to have web frames. If that first frame is a fiddly
little thing within two feet of the stemhead, then you can
almost guarantee all sorts of fun when you have to mesh and
cement that unreachable wedge shape. And since we are on to
web frames, how far apart are they? It is so much easier to
mesh the inside of a boat if a full width panel fits neatly between most frames. Space the frames closer—at 30 inches or
less—and the number of wasted strips becomes very expensive. Don't kid yourself that you can use all those offcuts in
out of the way places; they never fit anywhere but next door's
rabbit hutch. However, if your boat is wide and shallow like
mine, she may well need closely spaced frames to add support
to flat areas in the hull shape which might sag when cemented.
Nice curves resist sagging better and need less internal
framing in support.

33

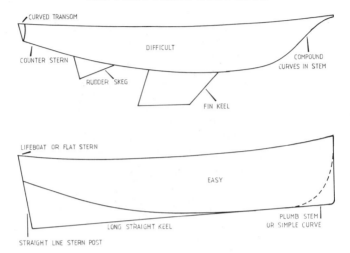

Fig 2 Difficult and easy boat shapes.

That's also the reason that many boats with counter sterns have those curved 'developed' transoms. But curved transoms are not the easiest to make and the setting up and bracing of counter sterns calls for care. Flat transoms with the rudder 'out of doors'—I'm back to traditional style again! —mean less work but you still have the bracing of the flat face of the transom to consider. As a result, when Jay Benford suggests that the pointed lifeboat stern is the easiest to build in ferro, you probably see why.

On deck, there are several features to notice, the most obvious of which is the coach-roof or lack of it. In order to save weight, many ferro boats are built with plywood decks and coachroof. These seem to work well as long as sufficient thought has gone into the way that wood meets cement: if not, that's where the leaks start. This is the reason that plywood is infinitely preferable to a traditional laid deck where timber expansion and contraction is so much more. The next design alternative is to combine a cement deck with plywood

34

coachroof and here again the joint between the two is of prime importance: a sizeable ferro coaming to which the house can be bolted with its lower edge an inch or two from the deck seems to be most popular.

You'll appreciate why many people like a flush deck in ferrocement: the structural integrity of a ferrocement 'cylinder' that is both strong and leakproof sounds very appealing, with the additional satisfaction that the hull is well on the way to being finished, directly after plastering. However, the plastering operation itself can sometimes be made more difficult by a flush deck. You can get around the problem of supporting the weight of all that setting cement but the actual logistics of getting a lot of cement and a lot of volunteers in and out of those all-very-seamanlike small hatch openings can present problems. Equally you will not have plastered much of the deck before it's so dark in there that it is very difficult to check on proper cement penetration, let alone produce a good plastered finish.

Talking about openings, do consider how timber hatches, cockpits and so on are designed if you are building in ferro because your joinery is not the best. Generally speaking, bolting to a cement coaming is easier than bolting directly to the deck—the fairest of decks can develop mountains when you come to plane timber to fit. However, if you use double coaming hatches of the Maurice Griffiths type with the outer coaming of timber and an inner coaming of ferro as an extension of the deck, even deck-bolted hatches can be leak-proof.

I do hope that you have not read these thoughts on design as categorical 'dos and don'ts': I give them only because it is nice to know what you are letting yourself in for. Certainly don't let any one of them put you off a design that you otherwise fancy; but they might help you decide between several. Equally, talking to other amateurs will produce some design points to notice, though you'll never find two who agree on the ideal boat for ferro or the ideal boat for the beginner to boatbuilding. However, approaching design selection from the standpoint that the easiest boat to build leaves you all the more mental energy for building her well, I offer a couple of suggestions.

Jay Benford makes a good case for the flush-decked double-ender as an easy boat in ferro though I think I would rather she had a small coachroof—like the Paul Johnson 'Venus Escape' class. With cement decks and coachroof sides on a boat somewhere between twenty and thirty feet long, the extra access during building through the hole to be filled by the coachroof lid would be a big asset. Her size might also incline me to a transom instead of a pointed stern—simply for increased deck space aft and better buttock lines in a sailing hull. If I was in a hurry, I might also settle for a straight stem. In the next chapter, I have included one or two designs which possess some of these characteristics, but any design based on the traditional English craft of the last century could be an easy proposition in ferrocement. There are also many well-known yacht designs, some quite recent, which have their origins in these tested boat shapes, as a glance through any British boating magazine will show. In the USA, the additional complication of a counter seems inevitable if one looks to traditional craft for inspiration, unless you search out colonial variations of British themes, such as Thomas Gilmer's *Blue Moon* or Lyle Hess's delightful *Serrafyn* for Lin and Larry Pardey.

Which construction, which designer, which boat? It's your choice but please don't make it quickly for you'll have to live with it for quite a while. Really find out what's available—from boating magazines and catalogues—and try to gauge what you get for your money. To start you off, I've sorted out a few designs from proven designers which might give you an idea of some of the possibilities of your first ferro boat.

3

'Go simple, go modest,
go small, but go'

Lin and Larry Pardey: *Cruising in Serrafyn*

It seems sensible to base this chapter on the assumption that you will build from a stock plan. As Bruce Bingham has pointed out, a one-off design which gave all the information a first-time boatbuilder might need would cost the earth these days: only by mass producing stock plans can designers supply the information and keep costs down. That being said, many of the stock plan designers realize that one of the joys of building her yourself is the production of a boat that's different from the rest and so they supply alternative rigs, keels, lay-outs and so on for basic hulls. There is variety and you can build an individual boat, though I'm aware that to some, there may be distinct similarities in some of the designs I've selected.

To try to account for my apparent partiality of selection, let me start with size. Very few of the boats I've chosen are over 30 feet in length and I have already made some comments about choosing a small boat as a first ferro project. To re-inforce this point, it might be worth adding that though there are lots of exceptions, a rough average of a year of spare-time building for every ten feet of boat length seems about right up to 30 feet overall, especially on cruising boats. Over this size limit, the extra costs and complications of big-boat fitting out seems to mean that every additional ten feet takes another two years: thus a 40-footer seems to run to five years on average, a 50-footer seven years and so on. Perhaps we're all a bit slow and leisurely in this corner of Cornwall but it means that not only does the builder have to maintain his enthusiasm and momentum throughout these periods, he is faced with the quite considerable decrease in any boatbuilding capital he might have by—at the time of writing—16 per cent per annum, due to inflation.

This cost factor is also responsible for what may seem to be a common style in the designs I have selected. Despite my moanings about the rising costs of ferrocement in Chapter One, I'm sure that many still fancy a ferrocement hull for its cheapness. If that is the case, it seems sensible to me to continue the cost-saving theme to the rest of the boat as well. No point saving money in the hull construction only to pay prodigious bills for epoxy resin filler to make that hull as smooth and glossy as resinglass. Thus I have tended towards traditional looking designs in the main. I think that they are easier to build, and boats that are close enough to their workboat ancestors also look right without a dazzling finish. These are boats which will not look shabby if cheaper timber and paint are used instead of the best stuff and varnish, and if the cement hull is not rendered glass-like but simply painted with a semi-matt pore-filling epoxy paint.

Bringing the same traditional approach to the rig also continues the cost-saving theme and accounts for what must seem a preponderance of gaffers. However, as I've said, ferrocement sailing boats in the 20–30-foot range are generally of medium to heavy displacement and this in itself is good reason for adopting the extra driving power of the gaff rig. However, more important to my mind are the cost savings when spars are grown sticks, and fittings are home-made from relatively inexpensive mild steel. In Britain, small firs can be obtained very reasonably from the Forestry Commission—in 1977, a 30-foot tree for a mast cost £15 for example —and the work of shaping up from an eight-square is particularly satisfying. Similarly when you have already mastered the elementary welding skills to build your hull, why not use them to make mast fittings from sections of pipe that you then take along to be galvanized. With a gaff rig, you can even take the cost-cutting further by making up your own wood blocks and deadeyes. However, it would be wrong to imply that Bermudan rig is out because it must always be expensive: Richard Hartley, Jay Benford and many others have some attractive boats rigged thus—and some excellent money-saving suggestions.

And Richard Hartley, of New Zealand, whose designs seem to be chosen more often by first-time amateur boatbuilders than anyone else's, is the man to lead my parade of designers. Hartley's *Ferrocement Boatbuilding* is not only one of the most practical of the ferro textbooks but also a complete catalogue of the author's designs for sailing and power boats between 27 and 57 feet in length. True, most of his designs are over my arbitrary length limit but his 'Coastal 30' displacement motor cruiser and his 'Tasman' ocean cruising motor sailer at 27 feet overall are within my range. Just over is a 33-foot 'Queenslander' motor sailer—one of which, with ferro hull, deck, coachroof, cockpit, etc., was sailed the 1,300 miles from Fiji to New Zealand in ten days—and the 'RORC 32', an ocean racing sloop.

One of these 32s, *Träumer* built by Wolfgang Schenk in Auckland, has been raced consistently and creditably with top-class Half-Tonners and as Richard Hartley wrote to me, 'She was racing against boats, the designs of which cost almost as much as all the materials in *Träumer*'. Another of the same class, *Moonbird* (see p. 19), built by Dennis Bailey as a cruising boat, has cruised from NZ to Fiji, to the New Hebrides, to New Guinea, to Indonesia, around Australia and further still: a cruise of over 8,000 miles, during which the boat survived several groundings and even a gas bottle explosion that lifted the timber cabin roof but left the ferrocement hull undamaged! Hartley puts it this way: 'Sooner or later, NZ boat owners make the 1,200-mile trips to Fiji or

6 Hartley's 'RORC 32' *Träumer*, built by Wolfgang Schenk in Auckland, has raced consistently and creditably with top-class Half-Tonners.

Australia or the 3,600-mile trip to Tahiti. These long distances do influence my cruising designs greatly.'

Richard Hartley also tells me that many of the smaller 'Tasman' 27-footers have been modified during building into commercial fishing boats for crays, gill netting or long-lining. However, a British amateur boatbuilder with dinghy experience but none in ferrocement, Ian Wright of Goodmayes in Essex, built the design as a yacht. He chose the optional bilge keel version which gives a draft of 3'0", rather than the 3'9" of the fin-keeler and opted for a timber deck and superstructure to save top weight. Mr Wright found the Hartley plans very detailed and easy to follow. As with many others though, he decided to diverge from them slightly and use 3 layers of welded mesh inside and out instead of the recommended 4 layers of chicken wire and he found welded mesh both easy to use and easy to fair. Thirteen months after starting work, the hull was plastered in one-shot with pre-packed yacht mortar by three professional plasterers and eight volunteers. Construction of the timber deck and cabin top is now well advanced and launching is anticipated in late '78.

Still in the Southern Hemisphere, another source of attractive designs is 'New Zealand Ferrocement Services Ltd', a company formed by Dr Gary Bowen and Ian Baugh, joint editors of the prestigious *Journal of Ferrocement* from 1973 to 1976, to market sets of stock plans developed from the custom designs prepared by naval architect Brian Donovan over the last ten years. Features of the construction methods they favour are removable timber shadow moulds instead of web frames, and standardized construction details on such com-

7   Richard Hartley's 'Tasman' 27-foot motor sailer of the type being
built by Ian Wright of Goodmayes, Essex.

ponents as rudders, stern tubes, masts, decks, internal joinery, etc. Ian Baugh explains that this use of 'typical detail' sheets helps the firm to supply *all* the information the first-time builder needs and still keeps the prices of the plans sets within reason. He goes on: 'As you know, describe something as being for "yachts" and the price becomes astronomical. Our detail drawings show how to build almost every item of gear on our boats, in many cases using methods of doing things which are almost forgotten. Building something obviously takes a lot longer than simply screwing on a bought item but, especially for people competent with their hands, this approach makes it possible for them to afford the boat they want.'

The range of Donovan designs available covers sailing boats, power boats and fishermen from 19 to 60 feet. Under 30 feet, there are 19- and 28-foot Bermudan-rigged yachts and at 30 exactly, a Sport Fisherman and a one-man longliner. Not to mention two other Donovan designs, one illustrated here. 'Tamure' is a 28-foot displacement power cruiser of the sort that Ian Baugh feels is particularly suitable for ferrocement construction since the weight of the hull—ferro throughout—gives an easier motion and means that large spaces within the boat are not wasted on ballast. A couple could live comfortably on this boat for extended periods with some home-style comforts: ferrocement water tanks are built in, as is a holding tank for recycling water from the shower, basin and sink. Though a 30-SHP diesel is suggested, smaller power units—down to 18 SHP—could be used.

The 27-foot gaff sloop 'Kapowhai' is designed for much the same sort of role: comfortable coastal cruising for a small crew. As Ian Baugh puts it, she is a traditional ship that the man who owns the latest racer may not appreciate but there are very few items, on or below her decks, that a capable amateur could not make for himself. The sail plan is especi-

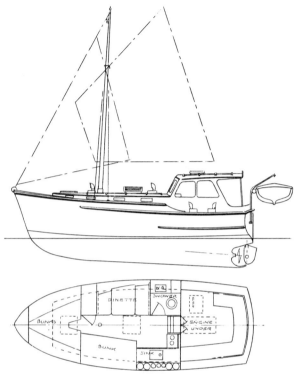

Fig 3 'Tamure', a 28-foot motor cruiser designed by Brian
Donovan for New Zealand Ferrocement Services Ltd.

ally designed for easy handling with a boomed self-tacking
headsail and lazyjacks to catch the lowered mainsail. As with
'Tamure', the hull, deck and coachroof of 'Kapowhai' are
entirely ferrocement.

The name of Robert Tucker is already known to boating
people in Britain and around the world: his little bilge-keel
sloop *Silhouette* appeared in 1953 and introduced a whole
generation to amateur boatbuilding in plywood. Times have
changed though and so have plywood prices and today,

Robert Tucker offers a whole new series of designs for ferro-cement. Many are full-size workboats, luxury power yachts and ocean sailing cruisers up to 70 feet overall: to my mind, boats to dream about until you have gained considerable experience of ferrocement boatbuilding. Certainly some look well beyond this amateur boatbuilder's experience, though I might be persuaded by the attractive 40-foot junk-rigged schooner *Island Sun*.

However, on a less ambitious level, Mr Tucker has some appealing small boat designs. The tiny Bermudan sloop 'Kloof' was originally designed for professional building but may well be within the capabilities of a conscientious amateur with boatbuilding experience in another medium. A boat for an entirely different role is the 'Fisherman 25', a robust deep-water workboat capable of carrying $1\frac{1}{2}$ tons of fish. Included

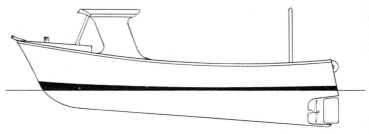

Fig 4 'Fisherman 25', a robust deep-water workboat from the board of British designer Robert Tucker.

in the plans are both optional engine positions and alternative rakes to the stern for stern or side working. A modified version of the boat shown here is now under construction in East London as part of the Government Job Creation Programme. A feature of all the Tucker ferrocement designs is that individual assistance is offered to each builder to help him prepare the best possible mortar mix from materials available in the building locality.

In contrast to the strikingly modern shapes of Robert

44

Tucker's designs, Percy Dalton specializes in re-designing the traditional craft of the last century for today's materials and needs. I suppose I ought to declare a sort of interest at this point because it was to Percy Dalton I took my rough sketches based on Slocum's *Spray* and he turned them into a boat. However, Percy's more frequent customers are Falmouth's oyster fishermen who still earn a living under sail, thanks to a far-sighted local bye-law that conserves fish stocks by prohibiting dredging under power. However, some of these craft are now over a hundred years old and for replacements—and new additions to the fleet—the fishermen come to Percy Dalton, though the high cost of timber now means that they ask for designs to be built in resinglass, 'C-Flex' and ferrocement, like the typical 28-footer illustrated here.

Fig 5 The 'Falmouth Working Boat', a 28-foot oyster dredger by Percy Dalton.

Percy Dalton.

Though these craft are essentially workboats and Percy Dalton is a professional's designer, amateur boatbuilders who have sufficient experience to work from a basic set of plans and are confident of their ability to learn the old ways of working a boat under sail are showing more and more interest in these 'traditional' designs. Certainly from the first ferro builder's viewpoint, the combination of a particularly easy hull shape with a dayboat-type layout which requires little joinery in the fitting out, all under a rig that can use grown spars and home-made fittings, makes for a boat that can be built both cheaply and quickly. Used in the sort of estuary for which it is designed and sailed by an adequate crew, such a craft could give a year or two's enjoyable day sailing before the addition of a pre-fabricated coachroof and cockpit as shown in the plans for the smaller 22-foot version (see p. 175, Appendix A).

Another designer with an interest in both fishing boats and traditional sailing craft is John French who at the time of writing lives and works in Essex but will shortly be emigrating to Bødo in the very north of Norway where he hopes to start building his own fishing boat designs for local use. Here in England, Mr French has prepared a number of designs for Ferro-cement Marine Services of Burnham-on-Crouch. The most recent example is a 24-foot cruising yacht, originally drawn for Roy Foram, an Essex yachtsman with a liking for the old gaff cutter rigged Itchen Ferry smacks of the Solent. With her straight stem, long keel and simple transom, this looks an ideal first ferro project.

Another designer with an equally attractive classical design in Ferro-cement Marine's folio is Alan F. Hill whose delightful 32-foot 'Burnham Bawley' has many similar easy-to-build features. Ferro-cement Marine's other traditional design, just on my 30-foot limit, is the cruising version of an 'Essex Smack', shown here. Though the stern may call for a little extra effort, the comfortable layout possible with a 10-

Fig 6 The 'Essex Smack', a 30-foot cruising version of a famous
East Coast boat type from Ferro-cement Marine Services
of Burnham-on-Crouch.

foot beam, the handiness of a draft of 3 foot 9 inches and the
appeal of the classical English rig will appeal to many I'm
sure. Along with other designs to 73 feet, Ferro-cement
Marine can supply 'skeleton' kits of all their designs with a
choice of web or pipe frames.

The designer with the biggest range of designs and the
widest experience of small boats in ferrocement must un-
doubtedly be the American designer, Jay R. Benford of
Friday Harbor, USA and I am particularly indebted to him
and his wife Robin for answering many queries over quite a
distance. The Benford range for ferro includes motor boats
and cruisers at 14, 17, 24, 27 and 30 feet, a 30-foot houseboat
called 'Waterbed' and twelve sailing boats between 12 and

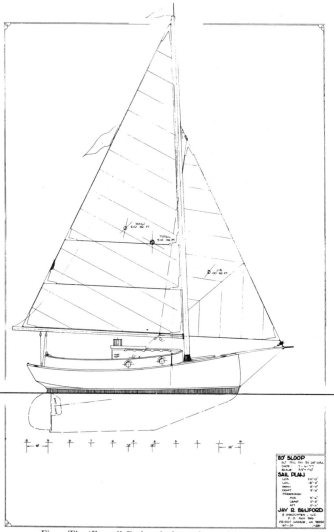

Fig 7 The 'Fantail Catboat', shown here with the optional
Bermudan rig, by Jay R. Benford of Friday Harbor, U.S.A.

48

30 feet, many with optional rig and layout permutations, not to mention thirty other designs for the material over my length limit. From such a wide range I can only touch briefly on a few.

Let me start by mentioning two jolly little motor cruisers, one only 14 feet long and designed as a marina tugboat, complete with wheelhouse, and the other, a 17-footer, a variation of the sailing hull of 'Puffin', the first of the very large class of 'Sphinx' catboats. With a beam of 7 feet and a draft of 2, this little cruiser has over 6 feet of headroom in the wheelhouse and will cruise happily at 5 knots with a 5- to 10-HP inboard engine. Of similar size, there is an 18-foot yawl (see Appendix A, p. 172) and another catboat, 20 foot this time, with a fantail stern and an optional sloop rig for dubious Europeans. Yet another 20-foot sloop has the straight keel, shapely transom and clipper bow of the traditional 'Friendship' sloop. One of the class, *Ragnar*, was wired up and plastered at the 1972 Seattle Boatshow and, finished to a high standard, became the Benford demonstration boat (see photo 1, p. 16).

Somewhat larger at 27 feet overall is the canoe-sterned Bermudan cutter shown here. She's a larger version of an equally clean-limbed 22-foot 'Knockabout' sloop and is designed for an all-mesh armature (no rods). She is what Robin Benford calls 'A more responsive sort of Colin Archer' and the light displacement should help her get to windward very well. At the same length, there is another canoe-sterned Bermudan cutter of entirely different concept: a broad-beamed flush-decked cruising boat designed for serious voyaging.

Looking equally capable, the largest Benford design to be included here exceeds again my '30 foot maximum for a first ferro boat' limit but since she is a particularly easy shape to build being a flush-decked double-ender—and very pretty into the bargain—I offer no further excuses. Based on the well-

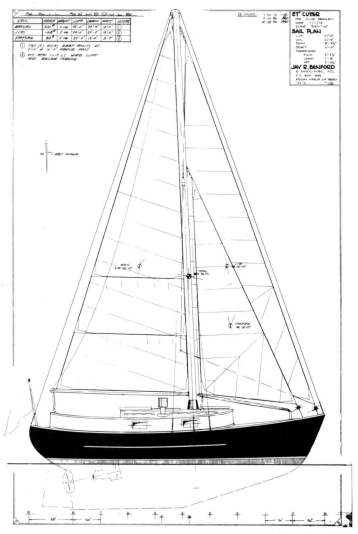

Fig 8 A 27-foot 'Double-ended Cutter', another Bermudan-rig
design from Jay R. Benford.

Fig 9 The 35-foot 'D. E. Gaff Ketch', another attractive and
easy to build design from the prolific Jay R. Benford that looks
capable of going anywhere.

proven Colin Archer sailing lifeboats of Norway, this 35-footer has over 6 feet of headroom under her ferrocement deck and a very liveable sort of accommodation plan, as you might expect from a designer who lives on a boat of much the same size himself. In the Benford Newsletter of September, 1973, Paul and Fae Miller reported that from lofting to plastering, the hull of their gaff ketch took just over a year's spare time work. This rig is my own favourite version but there is also a Bermudan cutter option. Tim Hurst, of Burlesdon, has taken the third option, a pole-masted gaff cutter, and his hull has now been plastered. Tim had plenty of praise for the sheer number of drawings in his plans package, in which he found lots of guidance on even the smallest details of construction.

That covers my design selection but, of course, it is by no means exhaustive. I would like to say a particular 'thank-you' to all the designers who helped me to compile this chapter. However, I must stress that their involvement here —or elsewhere in the book—does not indicate even their tacit approval of some of the alternative 'ways and means' that follow. From now on, I shall be dealing with the ways that I and other *amateurs* solved problems we encountered. Should you buy a stock plan from any designer, your best course must be to build the boat as he wanted it to be built, following his instructions as closely as you are able. But should your own particular circumstances or inabilities make one of the alternative methods that follow sound more attractive, do *please* check it out with your designer first. He may have an even better idea!

4
Twelve-inch rules—OK?

Let's start boatbuilding. For the sake of this particular chapter, I'll assume that you have already bought your plans though, as I've wearied you with already, I do think that it's wise to read this book through—and maybe one or two others also—before you part with any of the valuable green stuff.

Now the first step in building any boat is the lofting: drawing the brute full-size. You cannot possibly scale up a 30-foot boat from a drawing 15 inches long with any accuracy: an error the width of a pencil line could produce a monstrous bulge in the finished boat. So you must draw full-size each frame, the curve of the stem, the bends and kinks of the sternpost and propeller aperture and the real—rather than apparent—shape of the transom. You may also require to draw the various deck-beams, coachroof and cockpit sections and so on. It's axiomatic in boatbuilding that the more you do at the lofting stage, the easier things will be later on. Certainly it is possible to work out the shapes of beams, coachroof and cockpit *in situ* on the half-finished hull but it is a whole lot easier if you have done it all beforehand.

Having said that—and meant every word—I had now better explain why I am not going to describe to you exactly how to do it. Two reasons really. The first is that since the lofting process is pretty much the same for any boatbuilding material, over the years some excellent descriptions of the lofting process have appeared in print. The most quoted example must be the second chapter of the wooden boatbuilder's bible, Howard I. Chapelle's *Boatbuilding*. Since that appeared, there has been an excellent chapter in Bruce

Bingham's *Ferrocement: Design, Techniques And Application* and, most comprehensive of all, a superbly detailed and idiot-proof account of the whole business by Sam Manning in Issue 12 of the American magazine *Woodenboat*. Manning describes the lofting of a 26-foot gaff sloop, the 'Lubec' boat, from start to finish and though he is totally concerned with eventually building her in wood, he teaches the ferro builder all he needs to know in the process. Come to think of it, she would be a nice first boat in ferro—if the Woodenboaters will forgive such an alien thought!

My second reason brings us right back home to over-crowded little Britain. Even if you've digested all my ex-hortations to build something under that thirty-foot mark, a full loft of such a boat will still require a flat, level floor about 35 feet long and, at the minimum, a width of a couple of feet more than half the boat's beam, say, 6 to 8 feet at least. Spaces like that, even previously occupied ones, don't abound in the average semi. Of course, you could always borrow or hire a warehouse or church hall, pave it with sheets of ply or chip-board and draw her out there. The actual work is not that difficult once you get into it but the time taken, maybe 10 to 15 evenings, hardly makes hiring financially attractive. The trouble is that having drawn her out, you will then want to make some frames on the lofted lines and that must mean some welding somewhere. How many vergers do you know who will let you fill their church hall with welding fumes every evening for several weeks? And could you afford the hire costs if they would? Your costs would not stop there either, for the whole point of the full-size drawing is that it is a means of taking off shapes throughout the boatbuilding process and you have to hire the hall again—and hump eight sheets of ply there—every time you want to check something.

This is probably the reason why, of the several ferro boat-builders that I've pestered in recent years, I know of only one who did a full lofting job. His solution to the space problem

54

was to hire the boatbuilding site and erect his scaffolding frame at the beginning. With a polythene roof and a chipboard floor laid on temporary beams, his building frame became a moulding loft. It was particularly necessary to do a full loft in his case because he had designed the boat himself, during a college boatbuilding course, and he felt it wise to take extra care to get a fair hull. Was it successful? Well, the actual lofting work was not easy: first getting the floor level and then working to fairly careful limits with battens, tape and pencil with no protection at the sides of the scaffolding from wind and wind-blown rain. The result of his efforts, his boat, is a testament to his patience and tenacity but nice as she is, she does not seem more fair than the boats of we less hardy—and biased—souls who simply drew a careful body plan to the offsets of a professional designer.

So what's a body plan? Well, basically the full loft of a hull involves three viewpoints, just like your designer's lines drawing. On the same drawing, just to confuse you, he superimposes the view from the side (the profile), the view from on high (the half-breadth plan) and the view from the end (the body plan). Which end? Often both simultaneously! You see, he uses the boat's centre-line as the division and the right-hand half usually shows the shape of her front half, from amidships to the bow—known as the forebody—and the left-hand half of the drawing shows the afterbody, from the midsection to the stern-post. Our simplified version here should indicate what you have to pick out from the Clapham Junction of your lines drawing. The numbered lines are the 'stations', slices cut across the boat wherever frames will occur. The horizontal lines are the waterlines, slices cut lengthways through the boat, parallel to the Load Waterline (LWL) which is the line on which the boat will float—we hope!

Just to draw the body plan then requires a much smaller space than the full loft with profile and half-breadths—say a space a couple of feet wider than the maximum beam by a length that's about three feet more than the sum of the maximum draft and the maximum freeboard. These are the minimum dimensions and any space over this is especially valuable in allowing battens to be manoeuvred easily. Thus the body plan loft can be accomplished in a fair-sized living room, a double garage, a store room of some sort or even a level driveway or courtyard if you choose your weather: the boards required for a body plan can be picked up and packed away much more easily than the boards needed for the whole hull. If you are desperate for space, you may even like to consider a half-width body plan: drawing the stations of the forebody and stations of the afterbody at one side of the common centreline. This might be practicable if you are building a pipe-frame boat which necessitates little or no welding on the loft floor—in other words, you are simply bending pipes to the lines you have drawn. However, in an effort to get fairer pipe-frame boats, many of the designers who still favour this mode of construction close up the frame spacing quite considerably—sometimes they're 15 inches apart or less—and that's a lot of frames to draw and lines to differentiate. Web frames, at 3 feet spacings, would mean fewer lines but would involve welding *in situ*, and the confusion of a crowd of loft lines and burn marks might be indecipherable.

A method I used in the very tiny living room of a very tiny Cornish cottage is practicable however—just! With insufficient space to draw the forebody on one side of the centreline and the afterbody on the other, I drew both on the same side of the line but turned the afterbody upside down, making the LWL common to both. As the diagram shows, it does separate the lines a little better and you can improve things still further by drawing the forebody and afterbody in different colours. You still have something nearer to an Ordnance Survey map of a railway marshalling yard than a loft floor, however, and by the time you are welding up your last

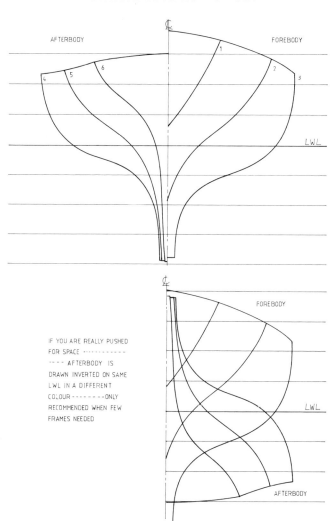

Fig 10 The body plan.

57

half-frame, only you will understand your lofting!

Still, this way we managed to get an 11-foot wide boat's body plan on three 8 by 4 boards which, stored on edge, took up little space behind the sofa. The biggest snag with this method is that having welded up two half-frames to each station line, you then have to join them together to make the complete boat frame. Thus, sooner or later, you have to get extra boards and find a working space as big as the full body plan. You won't need such a space for long but since you need it anyway, it's a good reason to draw a full-width body plan at the start, if at all possible.

You will probably need three sheets of 8 by 4 board for a 20-footer, six sheets if she is nearer to thirty. Whether you choose chipboard, hardboard or plywood depends on your personal preferences and your pocket—although hardboard is out if you have chosen web frames because it is too thin to hold the nails. For web frame making, your boards must be at least $\frac{3}{4}$ inch thick and a look at the relative prices of ply and chipboard at that thickness will help you decide. Ply is certainly nicer to draw on but any ideas that you'll be able to hide all those scorches and use the stuff when fitting out are generally over-optimistic. That leaves chipboard: look out for cheap offers at builders' merchants and search the shed for the remains of some light coloured emulsion to coat the boards so that the lines really stand out.

The timber merchants supply the lofting battens which will not need to be much over twelve feet long for a body plan of our size. A choice of sections helps: we used $\frac{1}{2}$ by $\frac{1}{2}$, and $\frac{1}{2}$ by $\frac{3}{8}$ and $\frac{1}{2}$ by $\frac{1}{4}$ on edge when we drew our hard-bilged *Spray*. As to timber, these days you have to manage with what you can get: Oregon pine or any softwood of a 'Clear & Better' grade (that means knot-free) should do the job, but get several because they have been known to break, and have them planed all round. Builders of small boats with particularly tight curves to draw might also like to look at nylon curtain

58

track or the plastic track for sliding hardboard cupboard doors. One amateur loftsman I know managed very well with lengths of springy steel rod, so if you have difficulties experiment a little. The main criteria are that the batten takes up a nice suent curve—meaning the sort of smooth curve you associate with girlie magazines but nowhere near as kinky—that it springs back after use and doesn't snap the first time you use it.

While you are doing all this shopping, you might also need to get coloured chalk, a ball of good old-fashioned string— not nylon twine—and either coloured ball-points or thin-point felt-tipped pens. Hopefully you will have a length of 2- by 1-inch timber around the place, around 3 to 4 feet will do, from which to make a primitive compass to draw right angles geometrically. All it needs is a nail through one end and a pencil-sized hole at the other. Perhaps you have also got a spring steel measuring tape—the kind with a lock that stops the thing springing when you don't want it to spring is handy if you are working alone—and finally a short straight-edge: a school ruler will do. Why so short? Well, long straight-edge battens are OK if made of something fairly inert: the long edge cut from a new sheet of ply for instance, but long straight battens of softwood inevitably become long warped battens of softwood. Better then a short straight-edge for inking in the chalk lines: any errors will be small and cancel each other out if you are careful.

To start, arrange your boards in the lofting space so that none of the straight lines you'll have to draw will co-incide with any of the edges where the boards butt together: one thing you can work out by scaling up from the designer's drawing. You will probably need an assistant when twanging in chalk lines, and the line to start with is the centreline. Once this is twanged, check it by pulling the string tight once more: if your twang on the string was not a vertical twang, your chalk line will be an ever-so-gentle curve. Do it again. When

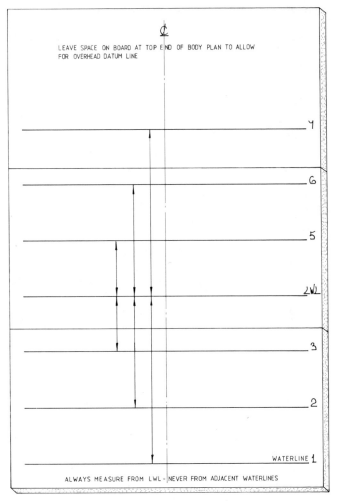

CHIPBOARD ARRANGED SO JOINS & DRAWN LINES DON'T COINCIDE

Fig 11 Lofting the grid.

it is right, using the straight-edge, ink it in the colour you have chosen for the grid pattern. Now mark on where the LWL crosses this centreline: arrange it so that any space left on the chipboard after drawing the body plan comes above the deck rather than below the keel; it will be useful later.

To draw in the LWL, you'll need the primitive compass. Draw two intersecting arcs at either side of the line with your compass nail at a couple of points on the centreline, equidistant from the LWL mark. The two intersections and your LWL mark can be lined up and your next chalk line twanged in: this Load Waterline becomes the datum for all further measurements, so it is worth taking extra care. All future measurements in order to space the other waterlines are measured from the LWL: don't think of the other waterlines as x inches apart, think of them as 1x, 2x, 3x inches, etc. from the LWL. The primitive compass will ensure that each waterline is at right angles to the centreline and your eye is a better judge than any ruler that the waterlines run straight and parallel. When you are satisfied that the grid is square, ink in the lines.

It's along these waterlines that you plot the points where each frame crosses—just like drawing a graph—using the measurements from the designer's table of offsets. The designer compiled this table of measurements from his original lines drawing and that was a full loft in miniature. Such is the skill of designers in scaling up offsets from measurements on a drawing that many give finished size measurements to onesixteenth of an inch. In the table of offsets, those finished size measurements will not appear as—for example—3 feet $11\frac{7}{16}$ inches, however: it looks clumsy even typed or printed. Instead, the convention with offsets is that the designer uses three columns of figures and a plus sign. Our example would appear on a table of offsets as 3—11—3 +. The first 3 and the 11 refer to feet and inches, of course, the last 3 may not be so obvious. It refers always to the number of eighths of an inch

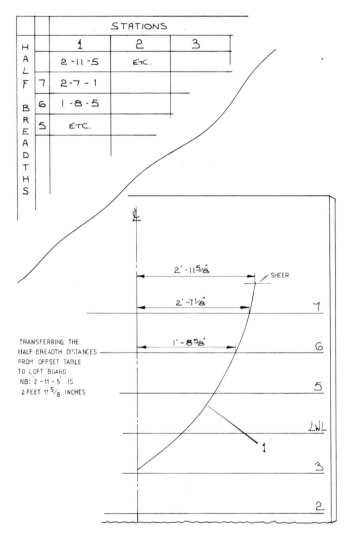

		STATIONS		
		1	2	3
H A L F B R E A D T H S		2-11-5	ETC.	
	7	2-7-1		
	6	1-8-5		
	5	ETC.		

2'-11⅝" SHEER

2'-7⅛" 7

TRANSFERRING THE
HALF BREADTH DISTANCES
FROM OFFSET TABLE
TO LOFT BOARD
NB: 2-11-5 IS
2 FEET 11⅝ INCHES

1'-8⅝" 6

5

⊥WL

1

3

2

Fig 12 The offset table, and the loft board.

and where an additional sixteenth is required, a plus sign is added. Thus the $\frac{7}{16}$ths in the example becomes —3 + : three-eighths plus one-sixteenth is seven-sixteenths. It should be said that not all designers work this finely: some are content to be accurate to an eighth. It all rather depends on the scale to which they drew out the lines in the first place: a small-scale drawing means less postage costs if it has to be sent to all corners of the globe. This being so, those commissioning a one-off design and collecting it from the designer personally might consider asking him to work to a larger than usual scale ($1\frac{1}{2}$ inches to the foot is a very easy scale to work with, for example): his offsets will be the more accurate and you'll have less fairing later on.

As in the diagram, your table of offsets will be divided into vertical columns, one column giving all the measurements needed to plot one station, i.e. one frame. It will also have intersecting horizontal columns each one of which representing one of the numbered waterlines, the sheerline and the keel bottom. So starting with frame one, using your non-recoilable steel tape, start to measure and mark the half-breadths on the appropriate waterlines—I suggest you use pencil and make short lines, not dots. I also prefer to add a foot to the half-breadth measurement and work from the one-foot mark on the steel rule: the little metal hook does not help accuracy if you are working on a flat surface. Mark in the top of the sheer and the bottom of the frame and then check everything. Twice.

If you are satisfied, it is time to draw the frame. Hammer in a $1\frac{1}{2}$-inch nail at each of your pencil marks leaving enough of the nail proud for the nail head not to catch the batten. With your batten 'inside the boat' push it out against the nails and hammer in more nails to hold the batten firmly against the others. Now get as far away as possible—you might even stand on a stool or step-ladder and look at the curve the batten forms, looking for any kinks or knuckles where the batten crosses a waterline. If you find one, remove the offending nail and the batten may well take up a more flowing curve without any help from you—sometimes only the smallest movement is sufficient to make it right. When you are happy, ink in with a different colour from that of the grid and start on frame 2. By frame 4, you'll be enjoying yourself and the rest will go very quickly—except for the one frame that causes problems that is: all we amateurs seem to have one such and it is nearly always in the run aft!

That done, you can start on the stem and stern posts and here is the first advantage of a long straight keel. While a complicated fin and skeg profile would need lofting, a straight line does not. Where your waterlines extend on either side of the body plan, you can draw the stem on one side and the sternpost on the other and include a short length of the keel profile—in effect, a diagonal line—on both. You may find the appropriate measurements on the lines drawing itself rather than on the table of offsets since there are usually fewer of them. Work is straightforward though a sharp turn to the forefoot may require the use of a plastic batten. Even if your sternpost is straight, you'll need to loft it anyway—partly to draw in a prop aperture and partly as preparation for drawing the transom.

Even the simplest of transoms usually has some rake to it—plumb sterns are rare—and this means that the waterlines on which the full-size transom is drawn must be spaced further apart, as Brian's drawing shows. For this reason, it is probably easiest to turn the chipboard over and draw a new grid; your lofting board will be rather crowded by now. The spacing of the new set of waterlines must be measured from the lofted sternpost—dimension B on the diagram—before you turn them over though. You'll probably find the half-breadths on the lines drawing again and fancy heart-shapes might again require the plastic batten. Even at this early stage, transoms are that little bit more fiddly and you'll begin

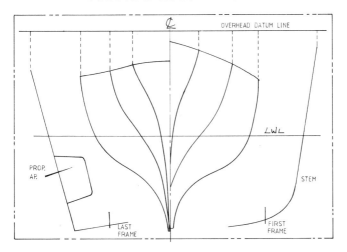

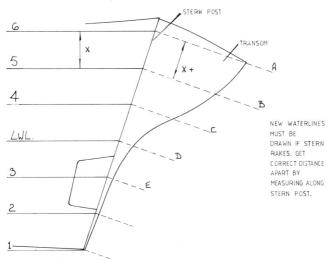

Fig 13 Overhead datum, end posts and transom.

to wonder why you didn't pick a double-ender!

By now your drawing is nearly complete, though some de-signers encourage you to draw in engine beds and water tanks to be built in ferro. Engine beds are OK as long as you do not make the assumption that your drawing is so accurate, you can make them full-size: better to allow for errors by making the ferro beds a few inches low and bolting timber bearers to them later. Timber is a deal easier to plane away than ferrocement. As to water tanks, my personal prejudice is that it's nice to be able to get to all parts of the hull if it is ever needed and integral tanks make this difficult at best. Worst of all are those tanks with ferro tops and tiny man-holes: just how are you supposed to cement the inside of a ferro tank top when your only access is a tiny hatch?

Instead, gentle reader, I suggest you bolt metal tanks to web-frame supports, and concentrate the last of your lofting energies on one last line which, to my mind is vital for a fair and bump-free hull. I reckon that many lumpen hulls start out being set up badly and anything that takes the setting up of frames beyond the bits of twisted wire stage must be an improvement. One way is to weld a piece of angle or water-pipe across each frame as a datum line and then, when you have the frames in the scaffolding framework, you can align these pipes horizontally with a spirit level. The biggest trouble with this system comes at the ends of the boat: a raking stem might mean that frame 1 does not even come below the waterline and others at the bow and stern may have so little beam at the LWL that these pipes are too short for practical aligning. For this reason—and others I'll get to at the meshing stage—several of us have now taken that datum pipe out and above the boat altogether by extending the boat's frames up from the sheer and, at the same distance from the LWL on every frame, welding the cross-pipe 'above' each frame.

So the last line on the body plan is the Overhead Datum

Line. Usually the highest freeboard is at the stem and your lofted stempost will indicate the closest that the Overhead Datum Line can be to the LWL. However, the greater that distance can be—that is, the higher the cross-pipes are above the boat—the less they will be in the way during the building process. On the other hand, it will also require a building frame that much larger and that bit more steel to extend the frames further. When you have sorted all that out and decided on the right distance, draw in the Overhead Datum Line and be sure you get her parallel to the LWL.

And that, as they say, is that. If you are still more than a little hazy about it all, I suggest you read this chapter through again. If after that the haze has turned into dense fog, don't bash on regardless, try a gin crate model. What you do is get hold of some thin ply—4mm is fine—and 'loft' the boat on it to a nice easy scale. Don't superimpose the frames, draw each separately and also draw the full profile, marking the stations. Cut everything out with a fretsaw and cut slots where appropriate so that the whole thing slots together like something off the back of a cornflakes packet. If it works, you'll know how to loft the big 'un; if not, take the model to one of the boatbuilders we chatted up in Chapter One. It's cheaper to get the model right before you go any further and when it is, you might even plank her with 1-mm model-making plywood: she'll encourage you from the top of the sideboard for months to come and the little woman will just love to dust her!

If you are still not happy about lofting, don't despair. Some designers, like Hartley and Samson, include in their plans-packs full-size paper patterns for all frames, stem, transom, etc. Of course, we amateur loftsmen, who can talk about nice buttocks until they call time, sneer at this back door to lofting. It's immoral somehow—like sliced bread and keg beer. Of course, you can be difficult and ask us what is actually wrong with paper patterns and we'll have to think

67

a bit before we announce that the paper might shrink in the post! The horrible truth, I must admit, is that I've seen fair and lumpy hulls built from paper patterns in about the same proportion as those built from home lofting; either system seems to work if you are careful. Take your choice.

5
Try it and see . . .

Before we start, a word or two about welding. You've probably read this far with the nagging worry at the back of your
mind that you can't weld. Perhaps for that reason, you have
already decided upon pipe frames for your boat. Maybe I
can dispel a few fears: the builders of the three ferro boats
nearest to my own had never done any welding at all until
they started those boats. Neither had I. All four boats seem
not to have suffered from this so far.

I'm pretty certain that you can weld too. You see, despite
all the excitement of the electricity, eye protection and pyro-
technics, the basic process is so simple that most pick it up in
less than half an hour. Furthermore the kind of welding that
you will be doing—basically downhand (that is, with the
work below you) and working with mild steel of moderate
sections—is the kind of work a welding instructor gives to his
pupils in the first lesson. You can pretty near build the whole
boat without ever acquiring more than the most primitive
skills. Even if one or two of your welds break eventually, it
won't be a major catastrophe: the best designed ferro armatures have an even distribution of moderately sized steel
framing with big chunks of steel deliberately excluded. That
means lots of minor welds but hardly any major ones. Furthermore in the finished boat, your welds will never be seen
—they had better not! The whole of the steel work will be
hidden in a cement coating which not only hides your ham-
fistedness for ever but ensures—with the help of the mesh—
that even your weakest welds are cosseted from stress. When
the cement is on, your hull is made of one composite material.

Probably the quickest way to learn to weld is to locate a friend who has one of those small 'portable' electric welding sets which give about 125 amps and can be run from the mains. If he will teach you, fine: you can skip the next three paragraphs. If not, you will have to borrow or hire one, but if you are really committed to this boatbuilding project, you may as well buy now. Hiring would cost as much and welding sets always seem to fetch a good price secondhand. Borrowing, hiring or buying, the guy you get it from will probably tell you which bit does what and if you are lucky, he may give you some pieces of scrap steel for practice.

Having lugged the thing to a suitable work-place—and now you know why I put inverted commas around 'portable' —ask your wife to keep the kids and the dog out of the way: their eyes will not be protected against welding flashes, your's will. The glass in the face mask should be so dark that you can hardly see the sun: if it's cracked or pock-marked, replace it. You'll also need a packet of 12-gauge electrodes (for welding $\frac{1}{4}$-inch rod or similar), a pair of welding gloves and a little chipping hammer.

The first thing to do is sort out the three electric cables. The thinnest of the three is probably the mains: the man who sold me mine said I should put a 30-amp fuse in the fuse box to cope with 'surge' when striking the arc; I forgot and have not blown a 15 yet. Of the two heavy gauge leads, one has a heavy clip to clamp on to a cleaned-up area of the work piece —rust or grease inhibits current flow—and the other has the business end in which you screw or clip an electrode. Most welders like to bend the rod to get a good angle and you'll discover how much suits you as you practise.

For $\frac{1}{4}$-inch steel, set the current flow at around 90 amps but before you switch on the power, it might help to do a dry run, without the visor so that you can see what you are about. The technique is to bring the tip of the electrode to just touch the area to be welded and then lift the tip of the rod about an eighth of an inch back from the work. This simulates striking an arc and maintaining the current flow: if your rod backs off too far from the work the arc breaks (you would strike again) and if the rod touches the work it sticks (release with a quick twist or switch off and separate). Once you have the arc running, your next move will be to rotate the tip of the electrode in tiny slow-moving spirals: practise this also while the power is off. Now, with the dark glass protecting your eyes, switch on and try it: *never* risk even a glance at the running arc without eye protection. Keep practising. When you have managed a few spirals, switch off and chip away the slag when it has cooled a little. Now try a better one. Then try one between two pieces of metal, chip away when cool and see if the joint holds. Keep practising. After a few dozen rods have been used, you'll be so good at it that you will be turning out significant modern metal sculptures—with all sorts to say about man's crisis of identity in the latter half of the twentieth century—faster than they can make motor cars and your art works will last longer.

You still prefer the idea of pipe frames? Well, OK, this is how we learned about water pipe frames. The books suggested hiring a plumber's pipe bender. We hired a plumber's pipe bender: a 'War of the Worlds' type three-legged contraption into which you insert your pipe, pull down a lever and bingo, there's a 90-degree bend! Since your bends need to be a whole lot less than 90 degrees, you have somehow to lean delicately on the lever and tremble a little. You need a very light touch but that's not the only problem. The books also suggest that you lay the pipe on the line on the lofting floor, take it to the bender, tremble somewhat, bring it back, test it against the line, back to the bender and so on. Well, if you like taking your exercise that way, I'm sure it's very healthy.

We found a much simpler way was to bend the pipe on the loft floor. First we nailed a couple of blocks firmly to the chipboard to wedge one end of the length of pipe against the drawn frame. Then we took two 4-foot lengths of $1\frac{1}{2}$-inch ID scaffold pipe with a T-piece connector screwed to the end of each so that the two pipes could be threaded on to the water-pipe to be bent, necklace fashion. With the two levers about 6 inches apart, one could be levered against t'other to bend the waterpipe a fraction. The levers were then moved along a few inches and the process repeated. After a couple of re-jects, we managed a pipe that more or less followed the line, though we were not very proud of it. Had we persevered, I am sure we would have improved and certainly bending the pipe on the board seems the right way to go. In Benford and Husen's *Practical Ferrocement Boatbuilding*, they describe an hydraulic pipe-bender made from a car jack which can work with the pipe laid on the loft floor and I am sure that such a tool would be well worth making. We only needed one bent waterpipe—for the stem—and were happy to start on the web frames.

As I have already explained, our boat is a version of Slocum's *Spray*, a shallow, beamy dish of a boat. In what must be an inherently weak shape, it seemed sensible to have the additional reinforcement of web frames throughout the hull and deep web floors to protect the keel structure as she takes the ground. Richard Hartley describes in his book how boats without these web floors have had their keels pushed up into the hull by violent grounding. Thus for our particular boat the advantages of web frames seemed essential. However, I can readily understand how the builder of a more slender yet curvy hull (sounds lovely!) would resent the loss of space to the webs and yet still see the value of the strength and rigidity they give the hull up to plastering. For such builders, an alter-native form of web frame, such as the Perry-Sortun type, which can be removed after plastering is ideal.

You'll need to buy few extra tools to make web frames. Apart from the welder, the only other expensive item is a pair of bolt croppers to cut the rod: using a hacksaw would take forever. You'll also need a good vice, a claw hammer, a few circles of $\frac{3}{8}$- or $\frac{1}{2}$-inch ply of diameters between 6 and 18 inches and an endless supply of $1\frac{1}{2}$-inch nails. Hopefully, you'll also have ordered a few thousand feet of the rod specified for frame making in your design. It is invariably mild steel but whether square section or round, whether $\frac{1}{4}$-, $\frac{3}{8}$-, or $\frac{1}{2}$-inch in diameter depends on the designer. I suppose $\frac{1}{4}$-inch diameter rod is common on most designs with standard web frames and any of the three sizes might be specified in the outer rods of the Perry-Sortun type.

Start by fastening down a length of rod to the inside of the line you have drawn for frame one. The rod should be long enough to stretch from the keel (or stem post) right the way

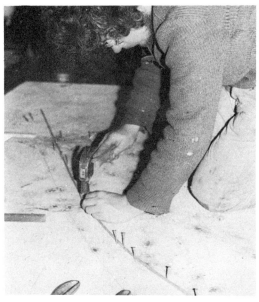

8 Carl Ronse locating the first rod of a web frame for a
Percy Dalton 28-footer.

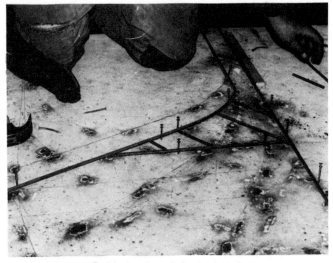

9 Positioning the rods for the deep-floor.

to the Overhead Datum Line and a little beyond. Start nailing at the keel, leaving sufficient of the nail proud for it to be clenched over to hold the rod tightly. Use nails at both sides of the rod and space them as closely as is required: be generous, 3-inch spacing is not too close on tightish curves.

You'll find that bending this small diameter mild steel is not at all difficult though care must be taken to avoid kinks. For much of the length, you will be able to tug the rod to the drawn line with your hands but for sharper curves—the reverse turn into the keel, for example—it may be necessary to use one of the plywood discs. Often it is sufficient to locate the disc where needed on the frame line, kneel on it and pull the rod around but in difficult areas it may be necessary to nail the disc temporarily to the chipboard. At such times, it helps if the keel end of the rod has been left over long so that a piece of waterpipe can be slipped over the end to give additional leverage.

74

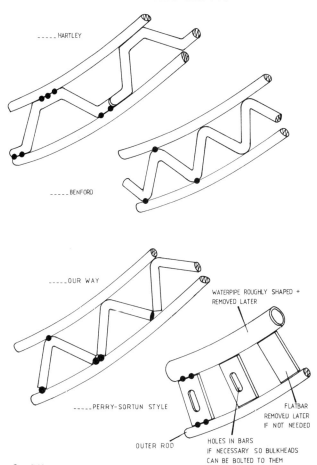

● —WELDS

Fig 14 Ways with web frames.

Before you nail down the inner rod which runs parallel to the first, you have to decide which way you will do the fill-in steel tracery that holds the two rods apart. There are at least three ways to go. Most common is the Hartley method: cropping off lengths of rod which are bent four times to make stirrups, as Brian's drawing (Fig. 14) shows. Brian made the frames of his own 42-foot ketch using this method, as did at least three other builders I know. All reported no difficulties, though they did mention that the production of ten to fifteen stirrups per half frame does take time.

At least a couple of other amateurs I know adopted Jay Benford's way with web frames. Instead of short stirrups he suggests a continuous zig-zag rod which is bent up in a jig made from a piece of steel plate with short studs tapped therein. Again these builders reported no difficulties.

Thus it is with no little embarrassment that I confess that neither Maggie nor I myself succeeded with either method! The problem was always persuading that second bend . . . and third and fourth . . . to lie in the same plane as the first. As a result neither our Hartley stirrup nor our Benford squiggle would lie flat on the lofting board. Thus we invented our 'squirrels': our personal idiot-proof mixture of both methods. Basically our squirrels are short rods with a single bend amidships so that, even with our workmanship, they must lie flat! First we cropped up lots of 9-inch lengths of rod—a friend with a mechanical cropper would have been handy here—and then a rod was fastened vertically in the vice with about 4 inches below jaw level. Out comes the good old waterpipe lever again which is slipped over the top end of the rod and given a tug. The test bed to check whether the squirrel has been bent to the right angle is simply a piece of wood with two lengths of parallel rod nailed to it at exactly the same distance apart as the depth of the web frames. Each squirrel is tested for a good fit between the rods and re-bent if necessary. I can understand that it may sound as if a lot of

76

10   Greenfield-type 'squirrels' in position; the inner rod is added.

testing and re-bending is required but it is surprising how quickly you learn just how much of a tug is required. After ten minutes, we found that we were bending squirrels to a snug fit first time. However, we are not making claims that our way is in any way better than Hartley's or Benford's: it simply suited us. It might suit you.

Whichever you adopt—stirrup, squiggle, squirrel or whatever—the next step is to lay these spacers against the rod nailed to the loft board. It may be necessary to nail down a continuous rod but in the general way, stirrups and squirrels just need laying in place with their 'feet' against the outer rod. The inner rod is then nailed down as was the first, touching the spacers. The whole thing is rather like a butch version of the old balsa strip and pins method of building model aeroplanes. Extra rods for deep floors, short transverse rods in the keel as bearers for large diameter keel rods, sole bearers, engine beds, tank frames, deckbeams and bulwarks can all be cut to size and nailed to the chipboard.

77

With the Perry-Sortun type of removable web frames the approach is slightly different, however. Instead of the rod to space the two parallels, flat mild steel bar—say $1\frac{1}{2}$ by $\frac{1}{4}$-inch —is used instead. Lengths are cut to the moulded depth of the frame and are fastened 6 to 12 inches apart, radiating inward (if you see what I mean!) from the outer rod of the frame. Closer spacing might be of value if you intend to fit a bulkhead in the boat at a particular station, for the bars are left as lugs to which the bulkhead is bolted. In such a case, it might be easier to drill the bars using a drill press before assembling the frame than attempting the task in the plastered hull. Patrick Silman, building a 28-foot oyster dredger of Percy Dalton's design, had no need of bulkheads at all so he was able to economize by using much lighter section flat bar ($\frac{1}{2}$ by $\frac{1}{4}$-inch) more closely spaced. That he was able to do so without any apparent loss in the rigidity of the frame is due

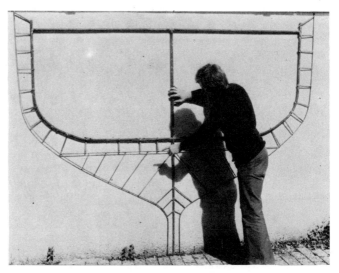

11 Patrick Silman's version of the Perry-Sortun frame has lighter section bars. Also note extra deep floor as cockpit sole bearer.

doubtless to the nature of the inner parallel in the Perry-Sortun type of frame. It is not rod, it's—you guessed it—good old waterpipe again! However, waterpipe bending here is a whole lot easier since it does not have to follow a drawn line but simply lies approximately parallel to the outer rod: as long as you can weld it to the spacing bars, that's sufficient. The reason is that meshing and cementing goes through—rather than up and over—this type of frame and when the hull is cured the waterpipe is cut away and perhaps passed on to another builder of the same design. Where bulkheads are not needed, the protruding stubs of bar are ground flush with the hull and protected with epoxy paint.

So with all the steel of the web frames, of whatever type, firmly in place on the chipboard, you can start welding. I found it best to start at the keel and work to the sheer, doing all the welds as I came to them—not going up one side and back down the other. This way the heat expansion seems to advance on a single front and does not create distortion. Where squirrels are not nailed to the board, they can sometimes stick and get lifted out of place by the welding rod. To cure this some sort of weight on the squirrel being welded may help: I used the bow fairlead from the rotting remains of a Salcombe smack! Where possible, make sure that a weld has taken before moving on to the next, that means you don't have to come back and do it afterwards with risk of heat distortion. You'll also soon learn that chipboard, while no substitute for apple logs of a winter's evening, can make a merry blaze. It also makes a particularly vile smelling smoke so it helps to put the fires out as soon as you can. Richard Hartley commends a damp sponge for this and others say it works well. Personally, I'm a coward in the simultaneous proximity of electricity and water so I adopted sand instead—those who have used both say it's less effective. Soon the desert sands, the procession of dying flames, the kneeling shuffle forward and the heady incense of burning chipboard begin to conjure up the atmosphere of some mystical Eastern devotion: 'Let's go for a pint!' I would cry mystically, after a couple of hours on my knees!

Before we left though, there was an essential task after we had put out all the fires. With one of those tiny tins of model-making paint and a kiddie's paintbrush, we marked on the half-frame the LWL line, the sheer, and the frame number. After the liquid refreshment, the task of removing hundreds of bent nails usually kept us busy for quite a while. However, we found that bending up sufficient squirrels, nailing down and welding the half-frame and removing the nails after it was cool—not to mention the administration of Mr Guinness's elixir—could all be accomplished in a not-too-frantic evening.

When both half-frames are completed, they have to be welded together, of course, and it's at this stage that frame making can be a little difficult. Extra care must be taken to see that the halves are accurately welded to mirror each other exactly and, rather than work amid the tangle of the body plan lines, I suggest you turn over the lofting boards: with only the transom to distract you, you should see more clearly what you are about. If you have not done so already, you'll need to draw out again the centreline, LWL and Overhead Datum Line. That done, you can lay the two half-frames in position and anchor them temporarily with nails. Now you start check-measuring. Check the half-breadths of both frames on the LWL and at the sheer and adjust them until they are right. Put in a few more nails. Check the distance from LWL to keel and LWL to sheer: you may even be able to tug out the frames to cure discrepancies here. When everything is good, nail down the half-frames really well.

Before you start welding though, there are still some essential pieces of steel to be added—not part of the boat but integral parts of the supporting and aligning structure. For this, I used waterpipe yet again but others have used good-sized angle or old scaffold poles with more success: the important thing is that they should be—and stay—straight. The first piece goes across the frame with its upper edge exactly on the LWL both to brace the frame and to provide support for staging on plastering day. It will need to be welded securely to the inner rod of the frame. Next comes the angle or pipe which is positioned with its *lower* edge exactly on the Overhead Datum Line. This length must be more than the maximum beam of the boat—not only will you want to weld it to the extensions of the frame rods, it will need to project at least 6 inches further on either side. These projections will take the weight of the frame during initial assembly and are part of the hull-support system throughout the building.

One more length of steel which not only supports but helps to locate the frame at the setting-up stage is the centreline pipe or angle. Centreline is a misnomer, however, since it is much handier if this pipe is located slightly to port or star-

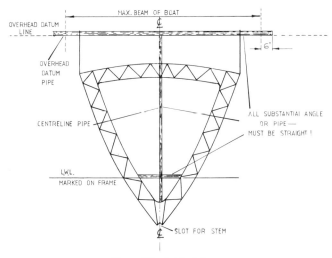

Fig 15 The finished frame.

board so that the edge of the pipe, rather than the centreline of the pipe, comes exactly along the boat's centreline. Which side of the line does not matter as long as you don't change your mind from frame to frame! Now with all this extra steel nailed down in the correct places, you can weld up the full frame.

As well as the frames of the boat, you will probably have to make up a transom in similar manner though many seem to prefer a thicker outer rod—$\frac{3}{8}$- or $\frac{1}{2}$-inch—or even the use of waterpipe. Similarly waterpipe may be used for the stem-post in a similar manner to a pipe frame. However, my own preference is for rod over pipe anywhere in a ferro hull and the next boat I build will certainly have a web-type stempost as in the photo (p. 88) of the Hartley 32-footer under construction. Luc Delahaie, building a 38-foot Colin Archer, used web-type posts at stem and stern with much success during armature construction and no apparent snags during plastering. As with frames, it is wise to leave stem and stern posts, if any, over-length at the upper ends so that they may be welded to the centreline structure of the building frame to provide additional support for the ends of the hull.

By the time you have pre-fabricated the kit of parts for your boat, it is as well to have a building site in prospect. Perhaps it is wise to start hunting after the successful completion of frame one. What to look for, some guesses as to what you will actually find and what to do with it once you've found it (!), we'll get to grips with in the next chapter.

6

Hang 'em high

You will need to look long and hard to find a site on which to build your boat. Nowadays, most of the good places to build a ferro boat seem to have a ferro boat in them. It seems that no small builder's yard is complete without the world girdler next to the corrugated cludgy. If she is nearing completion, perhaps a touch of vigorous and obvious assistance (feather dusting and rigging a seamanlike purchase for the Guinness bottle that christens her) might enable you to take over the site and the building frame also.

More likely, you'll end up trudging around the district like the rest of us. Tell friends and neighbours, relatives and creditors what you are looking for and have them search also. Look at every site they suggest. At this stage, it is as well to leave all those excellent ferro manuals emanating from the past and present colonies on the bookshelf. Their descriptions of what to look for in the ideal boatbuilding site will just depress you: Australasia and America are positively polluted by wide open spaces just asking for boats to be built in them, it seems. Here in good old cosy overcrowded Britain, you'll have to take what you can get or give up the whole idea, buy a colour telly and wait to die.

At the minimum, the absolute minimum, I would say your site must have three essential attributes. First is the old chestnut: a way out for the finished boat. Do not assume that the occupants of properties adjoining the site will be so enthused with the project as to demolish walls and chop down cherry trees when the time comes. If you are thinking in terms of craning the thing out, pay the crane-hire people

—now—to come down, see the site and tell you whether it's possible. Sure, road cranes can lift a lot heavier loads than your thirty-footer but that's when the crane jib is vertical. If the crane jib is lowered in order to reach over something to the boat, then that crane's lifting ability is reduced drastically. The hire people know what is feasible: do check with them before you start.

Derek Blundell's problems, none of his own making, when getting out his 45-foot Hartley 'Tahitian' might give you food for thought. The little builder's yard was sold and the new owner, not unreasonably, wanted Derek's three-quarters finished boat out of the way. However, though the yard's previous owner had told Derek at the start of boatbuilding that the yard would be hard surfaced, it was something that just did not get done. As a result, on boat-moving day the crane got bogged down in a quagmire of mud, sand and old bricks and could not make the lift. A month of hard work making solid standing for the crane followed and they tried again. This time the low loader got bogged down! Another massive bill! At the third try, things went better. She swung nicely up into the air, round towards the low loader and then the driver realized that one of the trailer's axles had broken! While he departed on a round trip of several hours to fetch a replacement boat trailer, it was simpler to leave the boat up aloft than re-locate her precisely on the keel blocks. Thus when Derek's wife, Sue, was persuaded to make a cup of coffee all round, she had to leap aboard from the top of a ladder held by volunteers and test the gimballing of the galley stove in earnest! Late that day, Derek's boat arrived at the new site five miles away: total costs for the whole business of moving approached £400!

Thus the second essential attribute your site must have is the lack of any time limit on the length of your occupation. If the chap who is renting you the site understands that you will be there as long as it takes, this removes a major source of future friction. Maggie and I were especially lucky in finding a really kind and helpful boatyard owner, Ray Allerton of Penryn Bridge Boatyard, who had a corner of the yard where we could build out of everyone's way. A friend of ours at a neighbouring boatyard had the opposite fortune. Unknown to him, he was given a site by Boatyard A which was the subject of an ownership wrangle with Boatyard B. It suited yard A to have the site occupied and they charged a modest rental accordingly. However, as soon as the squabble was resolved and while the boat was unplastered, they decided they wanted the site for other purposes and quadrupled the rental fee. In other words, if you can get anything in writing as to who owns the site, and the rate you must pay, do so.

Do not think that you are bound to be in the clear if you build on land you own, however. One Yorkshireman had a four and a half year battle with his local councillor neighbour throughout the building of his boat in his own backyard: the councillor did not like the view! However, I'm told that if you have the stomach for such things, you can build your boat despite opposition from local bureaucracy. Apparently you simply write letters to them: each takes so long to get a reply that it buys you six months more building time. But it is not a way I would fancy: I'm not building a boat to see more of bureaucracy.

However, it gives me a nice link to site attribute number three: the site must be as close to home as possible. As Mike Robson who built *Galowa* puts it: 'You move the boat only once; you go to and from the site a million times.' It is worth tolerating all sorts of other setbacks for a site on which you can fit in a quick half-hour's wire-tying while waiting for tea. If working on the boat means loading tools into the car, perhaps a drive of several miles, unloading everything and pulling covers from the gear you have hidden from passing pilferers, then you will only consider boatbuilding when you have several hours of free time ahead. You may end up only working at week-ends and then the time it takes to complete your boat will lengthen immeasurably. I think I would even change my mind about the design I had chosen, if a shorter, taller, higher, longer, fatter, thinner boat meant that I could build in my own back-yard.

Those are the three essential attributes the site must have to my mind. Not absolutely essential, but very nearly so, are several others. First of these must be an electricity supply: not only is electric welding simpler, you cannot drill or grind your hull effectively without power tools. However, Brian Hancock who drew the diagrams for this book, got around the lack of mains power with a small portable generator that lived in the back of his van. Equally, it is nice to have a water tap nearby: you'll certainly need the stuff for plastering and curing. Though again, it is possible to manage by collecting and filling old water tanks for plastering day and using a curing spray on the wet cement hull—more of that later. As to other nice qualities your site could possess, proximity to a builder's merchants is really handy because you can waste a deal of boatbuilding time travelling to fetch the odd bolt, screw or whatever. By the same token, don't build anywhere near a yacht chandlers: you'll be broke before the boat's half-finished! Finally, if at all possible, don't build in full view of the public. Oh, it's nice to strike nautical attitudes for the local dollies going to meet their boyfriends of an evening but can you face a million repetitions of the inevitable 'Will it float?'

I seem to have talked at some length about finding a building site but, as you'll appreciate, it is a place that you'll see quite a lot. Many builders I know became quite despondent before finally finding somewhere . . . or, rather, anywhere. Many accepted very difficult conditions to have some place to build: one, locally, had the tide cover the feet of his building frame twice a day. Do start looking for a site early in the hope that you'll find the ideal but when you end up

settling for some obvious inherent setbacks, don't despair,
you've joined the club.

Once found, the first step on the site is to mark out the
rectangle that the scaffold cage will occupy. Though other
books advise it, I know of no amateur who went to the bother
of laying concrete hard standing on the site. As long as you
provide healthy foundations for the blocks which will support
the finished hull, the additional expense is unnecessary. Be-
sides, soft earth is much kinder to tools dropped from great
heights and to feet that seem to be forever walking round and
round the boat. You will notice when discussing site attributes, I left to your good sense that the space must be big
enough and to me, that means an absolute minimum of two
feet of clear space all the way around the boat, inside the
building frame. Don't forget also that outside the frame,
you'll need extra space on plastering day for sand heaps,
cement mixing and so forth.

I've also assumed that you will use scaffolding for the
building frame, though, of course, you can use timber if it is
available. Richard Hartley's photograph of one of his 32-
footers building shows a typical timber frame and his book
gives details of suitable 'scantlings' for their construction.
Timber has the advantage that polythene sheeting can be
fastened easily to the structure to provide shelter from wind
and rain, but with the price of second-hand timber being
what it is, it's an advantage that most must forgo. Only two
local amateurs have used timber in my district: Derek
Blundell built a massive Hartley-style structure with gable
ends big enough for his 45-foot boat to stand four feet off the
ground. Covered over with polythene, when the evening sun
caught it, it stood out from the surrounding countryside like
some futuristic floodlit cathedral! With less sophistication,
another chap erected a stockade of tree trunks, each 8 inches
in diameter and about 15 feet high with another three feet
set deeply in concrete. The poles were bought very cheaply

87

12 Very neat timber building-frame for Dennis Bailey's *Moonbird*.
Note web-type stempost and keel profile.

from the Forestry Commission and across them were second-
hand RSJs notched into the uprights. What there was of it
was enormously strong but a denser structure of less robust
material would have provided better all-round support.

So that brings us back to scaffolding and to describe it
properly, it seems simpler to use scaffolder's terminology.
Thus, uprights are called—would you believe?—uprights,
horizontals are runners, diagonals are bracers and short
lengths to support walkways are pudlocks. Thus having
measured how large a site your building frame may occupy,
the next step is to draw a quick plan with side and end eleva-
tions of the building frame. In drawing this, you can space
the uprights at up to six feet apart along each side of the boat
and still have sufficient support, it seems. Assuming no overhead obstructions on site and no local councillors in the im-

mediate vicinity, the higher that you can make the building frame, the better. It is so much less neanderthal to walk the decks erect and more important, so much easier for the plasterers if the boat is high enough for them to work comfortably under the turn of the bilge. Naturally, all this height means more scaffolding to buy or to hire. You can work out precisely how much you will need when you draw in transverse runners across the tops of each pair of uprights, at least one and possibly two runners down each of the long sides and short bracers on every alternate upright leaning into the building frame. If you can afford it, any extra scaffolding which can be used as long bracers on the sides of the building cage, will give the structure lots of extra stiffness.

When you have worked out how many of each length you'll need, don't forget to count the number of couplings, right angle and swivel, that you will need. Whether you hire or buy depends on your pocket but it may pay off if, as a first

13 Twin 28-foot working boats in a common building-frame: the left-hand boat has the outer layer of mesh applied roughly ready for tying, while on the right-hand boat, tying is well advanced.

move, you check the small ads of the local paper and ring round building firms and scaffold hire companies to see if they have any used scaffolding for sale. Two of us sold the second-hand scaffolding we bought for building our boats at more than we paid for it!

Exactly how you erect your scaffolding will depend on the shape of the structure and this might well have been indicated by the designer. Failing this—or if you fancy the Overhead Datum system mentioned in the last chapter—this is the way we tackled it. Our first step, once the positions of each upright had been pegged out, was to set the four corner uprights in a couple of feet of concrete, leaving each to set overnight while tied erect to a hired DIY scaffolding tower. This move was by no means essential, of course, but Maggie and I built the frame between us and it was so much easier than one of us holding an upright erect while the other dashed about coupling on bracers to hold it there. When you start with four uprights solidly in place, the rest comes so much easier. Those four concrete feet were also a comfort when the whole structure swayed a little in our Cornish gales. The rest of the frame building followed a logical pattern: uprights first, then bracers, then runners. Finally we added the transverse runners—the ones that formed the top of each portal frame—roughly at first, and then each was aligned precisely level with each of the others.

This alignment must sound a great deal more difficult than it really is. In fact, it went surprisingly easily. From the safety of our hired DIY scaffolding tower, the correct height for the transverse runners was marked on to one of the corner posts in paint. Then we bought 50 feet of transparent garden hose and tied one end of it alongside the marked corner post, with the end above the paint mark. The other end of the hose went to be tied to each of the other uprights in turn as they were marked also. To get a precise level, one of us went to the marked corner post and poured inky water into the plastic

14   Transparent garden hose containing inky water in use as a level.

hose until the water level rose to the level of the paint mark, a
few moments wait while bubbles dispersed and then the other
marked a new upright at the level of the water in the other
end of the hose. I know it sounds rather primitive but it is
possible to align all the transverse runners remarkably well
with this system—if you don't believe me, hire a Cowley
Level from a builder instead.

   You can check how good your alignment is when you
fasten a length of angle across them down the middle of the
scaffold frame to act as the boat's centreline. Having lined it
up with taut string, we fastened the angle to the scaffold
poles of the transverse runners with simple U-bolts, home-
made from $\frac{1}{4}$-inch mild steel threaded rod, sold in five-foot
lengths by our local steel stockist. Of course, if the scaffolding
is your own, you may prefer to weld the angle to it after
grinding off the galvanizing. But it is essential that you don't
get any heat distortion of the straight line and even more im-

portant that you *don't weld it yet*! The angle will have to be removed to get the frames into place and replaced afterwards. On our building frame, the weight of the boat frames and eventually the whole unplastered armature, was carried on three 4 by 4 bearers which ran parallel to each other across the tops of the portal frames along the full length of the scaffolding (see photo 16). The centreline angle has to remain in position in order that the two outer bearers can be correctly located at the right distance from it: in our case the maximum half-beam *plus* 2 inches. With these timbers positioned and fastened—again with home-made U-bolts—the centreline angle was removed temporarily in order to set up the frames.

So, one Sunday morning when the sun came out, we spent an exciting couple of hours juggling each frame up between the scaffolding and the timber bearers until the ends of each Overhead Datum pipe could rest securely on the bearers.

15   Maggie and assistant setting up the frames on the author's *Spray*.

With the centreline angle on the ground we marked off the positions of the tips of stem and sternposts and then all the frames between and then the angle was slotted back into place overhead and fastened. Then the dangling frames could have their centrepipes butted against the centre angle of the building frame and simultaneously be correctly spaced by alignment on the appropriate marks. Our idea was that the frames should be located and supported at the same time and, with some minimal fiddling, it worked! True there was more fiddling—and measuring—to come but it was nice to slot all the frames into place like toast in a toastrack: with some imagination, we could 'see' the whole loaf . . . or rather, boat: *Spray* isn't that full-ended, despite what our friends say!

Before the final positioning of each frame we inserted the third 4 by 4, in sections, by threading it at one end of the building frame. Precise location was not important, for once, since it simply took the load of each Overhead Datum pipe somewhere near the boat's centreline. Then came the check measuring. First the mid-section frame was set up precisely

16 Chris and Robert wire-tying on *Spray*: the frame suspension system can be clearly seen.

93

at right angles to the centreline of the boat by measuring two diagonals from the sheerline at each side of the frame to a common point a little way further along the centreline angle. Once positioned correctly, the frame was locked into place with 4-inch nails thumped into the 4 by 4s, though the nails were not clenched over to hold the Overhead Datum pipe tightly until a check had been made to see that the frame had not acquired a list to port or starboard. This was done with a spirit level (the hose was used successfully on some frames) across the LWL pipe and any corrections necessary were accomplished by packing up or cutting away the timber of the 4 by 4. When everything was right and the frame had been checked with a plumb-line also, the nails were clenched and additionally, the centrepipe of the frame was lightly tack welded to the centreline angle of the building frame. We found through experience that it's no good just positioning the frame correctly, once it's there you have to lock it in place so it cannot move later. More and more checking followed as subsequent frames were positioned and fastened in place: not only had each frame to be true unto itself, it also had to be true to *all* the others.

Next came the stem and sternposts, initially clamped to the centreline angle by the support rods and located to adjacent frames with twists of soft 2mm wire. At every stage of the final positioning of the stem and sternposts it was essential to test repeatedly with plumb bobs that *all parts* of the posts are on the centreline of the boat. To our cost, we found it was possible to have the tip and foot of our curved stem aligned correctly and still have the centre of the curve sagging away off centre. When all was OK, the posts were welded to the centreline angle overhead and the nearest frames.

Last came the keel and here I won't weary you with what we did: suffice to say that it was a contraption of my own devising built of the dreaded waterpipe on an expensive timber former. Not just that my system was unnecessarily

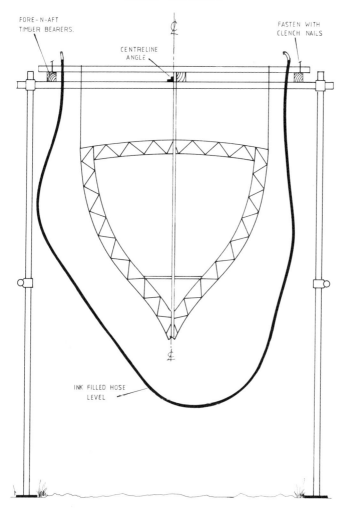

FORE-N-AFT
TIMBER BEARERS.

CENTRELINE
ANGLE

FASTEN WITH
CLENCH NAILS

INK FILLED HOSE
LEVEL

Fig 16 Setting up.

95

complicated, it didn't work so well either. Luc Delahaie saw the trouble we had and used an entirely different system on his boat: different, that is, in that his was both simple and successful. As I took care to mention earlier when describing the fabrication of the keel ends of web frames, he had the good idea to omit stirrups in this region and substitute short horizontal rods, parallel to the LWL. When all the frames are in position, these rods form miniature racks and by standing at the heel of the boat, it is a simple matter to feed in

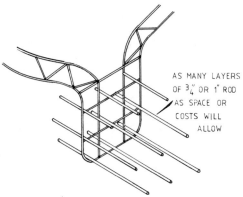

AS MANY LAYERS
OF $\frac{3}{4}''$ OR 1" ROD
AS SPACE OR
COSTS WILL
ALLOW

Fig 17 The simplest keel.

lengths of $\frac{1}{2}$-, $\frac{3}{4}$- or even 1-inch reinforcing rod in tiers. With all the rods spaced out nicely to ensure good mortar penetration—no closer than an inch, say—a keel formed of three or only two decks of rods, maybe three or four rods per deck, must be immensely strong. It will help to keep the web frames vertical if one or two of the outer rods are welded to each frame but for the rest, wire ties or spring clips suffice: those rods won't go anywhere.

And that's her set up. I know I've not mentioned blocks under the keel yet but there is no hurry. She can hang happily a while yet.

17 General view of the author's *Spray* under construction: that flimsy polythene roof lasted until the first Cornish gale!

7
Be fair!

I'll bet that you don't waste any time between the setting up
of the frames and fastening on the first stringers: you'll want
to see her shape. If you recall, stringers are generally fore
and aft rods only on boats under 30 feet, usually between
3 and 6 mm diameter. You may also remember that they
can be either mild steel, hard drawn or high tensile rod. Just
which depends on your designer—and you; for, with his
approval, it ought to be possible to substitute one type of rod
for another without affecting the weight of the boat. Having
said that, personally I would be very reluctant to use mild
steel stringers on any ferro hull, even if they were recommended by the designer.

Those who make web frames will find out just how
amenable to bending and welding is mild steel rod: it is these
qualities that make it so nice to work—when making web
frames. But when it is used for stringers, it is these same qualities that cause all the problems. The way that even 6-mm
rod can be kinked with hand pressure alone makes it totally
unsuitable as a material which must take up smooth flowing
curves. Similarly, the ease with which it can be welded might
encourage the amateur—and maybe a pro or two—to weld
the stringers to each frame. Not only is this totally unnecessary from a strength point of view, but in the one boat I've
seen built in this manner, the welds produced a noticeable
quilting effect along each rod. Seemingly, as the rod expands
with welding heat it bows outwards and when it cools, it does
not contract by the same amount; thus the quilting. True it
is possible to kink these bows vertically to remove some of

the horizontal 'belly' but what a lot of work when other types of rod are so much better.

Readers of the various ferro textbooks can be forgiven for some confusion as to the exact nature and differences of the two springier types of rod. Chris Cairncross sets the scene by describing the two types as round mild steel which has been heated and rolled, and square-sectioned mild steel rod which has been stretched and twisted cold. Jay Benford mentions high tensile wire and smooth, hot-rolled mild steel. Richard Hartley talks about hard-drawn wire and bright cross welding steel. And just to complete the confusion, my steel supplier spoke of hard-drawn and high tensile!

Since they all presumably know what they are about and the confusion is due to variations in local terms, perhaps the best thing is to go and see what your supplier has in stock. You'll soon identify the square stuff that has been twisted and also the rolled rod which will probably have transverse ribs on opposite sides of the rod—if you will allow that round rod can have sides at all! Both types should have similar strength around the 60,000-lb mark, though if the guy in the stores will allow you to flex a piece of each between your hands, you may find that the twisted rod is stiffer and more resistant to bending than the round; it may also be more expensive. If either, or both, come in rolls rather than straight lengths, ask the supplier if he will straighten it for you. Many can. Derek Blundell bought his rod in rolls and had no end of fun converting it into kink-free straights. If you have a straight choice, you may, like Brian Hancock and myself, opt for hot-rolled round rod: it has enough spring in it to take up suent curves but it does not seem to fight back quite so vehemently as the twisted sort. As ever, be guided by your designer. As to the lengths in which you buy it, transport considerations become important here. I know from bitter experience how loaders at the stock holders will blithely kink and coil beautifully straight 30-foot rods to get them aboard

99

an 18-foot wagon! Insist that the rods are delivered straight and accept any length limitations that the size of their delivery truck imposes: if they've only got a Mini pick-up, shop elsewhere!

With the stringers on site, the first dozen or so can be fastened to the frames. Fastening is generally by soft steel wire—16 gauge, for instance—which is twisted tight with pliers to hold the stringer to the frame rod. However, this is a time-consuming operation and we were very grateful to Stan Goldman who showed us the spring steel reinforcement clips

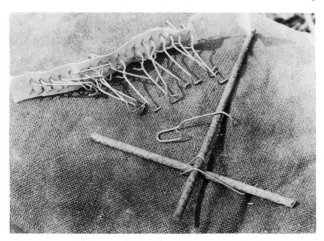

18 Spring steel reinforcement clips are the fastest way of attaching the stringers.

he used on his 22-foot 'Falmouth Working Boat'. These little clips are not expensive and can be bought to connect any pair of rods of specified sizes. They can also be removed and used again if mistakes occur—which they do. Using these, Maggie and I could attach half a dozen full-length stringers to each side of our 33-footer in an evening.

It is a mistake to assume that all your frames are fair and you can slap on stringers at a rate of knots and it is also a mistake to assume that if you find a fault, you cannot correct it. We started with the first half-dozen stringers, just below the sheerline, making sure that work progressed evenly at both sides to guard against distortion. The rods were clipped to each frame and because we were using 20-foot rods on a 30-foot hull, the necessary overlaps were wire-tied. The overlap, arranged so that it did not produce a bulge in the hull, was about 12–18 inches long and wire-tied in at least a couple of places. We also took care to see that the overlaps did not come at the same point in adjacent stringers by staggering the joints wherever possible. At this stage, the stringers were left 6 inches overlength at stem and stern and the ends were temporarily wire-tied there. With another belt of half a dozen stringers clipped on at the turn of each bilge and our stringers spaced at 2 inches, we had two foot-wide strakes on either side of the hull and checking could begin.

The first check must be to see that all the frames are square to the centreline of the boat (measure the diagonals) and that none has bowed athwartships: a pre-disposition of web frames of light-section rod and little transverse stiffening due to flimsy LWL members. Spring clips allow the outer edges of the web frames to be tugged into their correct positions and yet the six at the turn of the bilge seem sufficient to hold the frame from springing back again. An idea from Tim Hurst's Benford 35-foot Colin Archer type double-ender is to weld on temporary mild steel stringers at one-foot spacings to hold the web frames from flopping fore and aft. Conventional stringers were then attached between the mild steel ones and then the mild steel was cut away. While you are using mild steel, it is a good idea when you are sure that all frames are square, to attach fabrications for engine beds, water tanks, etc. at this stage. Doing these now, you weld such things in place while standing on a box on the ground; if you wait until all the stringers are in place, it's a great deal more difficult to work carefully.

Meanwhile, back at the stringing: at this juncture, we bought a dozen 20-foot ribbands (battens) of $\frac{3}{4}$ by $1\frac{1}{2}$-inch Clear & Better Oregon Pine. Tackling first the forebody of the boat, then the afterbody, we wired these ribbands to the frames of the boat, spacing them evenly over the areas not occupied by the first dozen stringers. Then we looked carefully. The ribbands made it possible to check whether the finished hull would be fair before all the stringers were in place and it was too much trouble to make corrections. As it happened, our forebody was perfectly good but when we re-wired our ribbands to the run aft, we found a 'wave' right in the middle of the *Spray* hull's best feature.

Though there was only a depression of around $\frac{3}{4}$ inch, it was certainly noticeable and I did not want the plasterers to have to correct such faults with additional cement. The smaller the ferrocement boat, the more essential it becomes to have a perfectly fair armature with no need for cosmetic infilling on plastering day: you cannot afford that extra weight. We found that the offending frame was wrong over about two feet of its length on either side of the hull. In our case, it was a depression but it could equally have been a bulge.

The technique we developed to cure the fault goes like this. First, bring all the ribbands to lie across the offending area, wire-tying them tightly to frames ahead and astern of the 'lean' frame but not to the frame itself. Surgery follows by snipping the diagonals of the squirrels (or squiggles or . . .) with the bolt croppers so that the inner and outer rods of the web frame are now unconnected in the offending area. It may then be possible to tug out the outer frame rod to touch the ribbands—in other words, to its correct position. If not, the outer frame rod will have to be severed some place and then, of course, it can be pulled into the correct position with no difficulty. Making good involves re-welding the various cuts you have made, where necessary using splints of $\frac{1}{4}$-inch rod to bridge any new gaps.

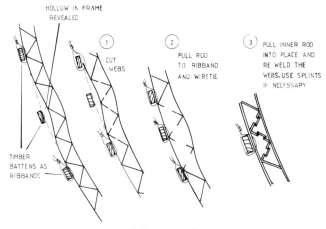

Fig 18 Fairing the hull.

Needless to say, similar surgery could be used to correct a frame that is too 'full' though this might mean removal of short sections of the outer frame rod in the region of the bulge. As long as plenty of support in the form of tightly fastened ribbands is available, it would seem quite practicable to repair any moderate humps and bumps in this fashion. Of course, removable web frames of the Perry-Sortun type would require the transverse bar to be sawn through near the outer rod but the general technique should work just as well. About the only type of frame it would not be able to help, it seems, is water-pipe. Of course, it is obviously a whole lot better from all points of view to draw the boat fairly in the first place but if a full loft is impossible for reasons of space, the body plan alone plus this later use of ribbands and corrective surgery can help you achieve what my cynical woodenboating friends say is a figment of my imagination: a really fair cement boat!

When you are really satisfied that the finished hull will be boat shaped and not bump shaped, the rest of the stringers can be clipped in place. Upper stringers will follow the sheer but if this is the pronounced curve found on many traditional craft, it is as well to start flattening that curve in the stringers progressively after the turn of the bilge. Before too many are in place it is a good idea to start attaching the stringers to stem and transom. Luc Delahaie, with a web stem and stern-post on his double-ender, was able to use spring clips here also, clipping the stringer to the inner rod of the web post. However, most still use rod or waterpipe for the stem and transom and the ends of the stringers will need to be welded in place.

Welding hard-drawn or high tensile rod is not easy. The rod becomes very brittle if heat is applied for any length of time and it is all too possible to burn through the rod completely. Thus a quick tack, just enough to anchor the stringer, must suffice. Whether the stringers are left overlength and bent round the stem rod to overlap with stringers from the other side or cut off at the stem rod itself depends on your preference and the design. Too many overlaps at both sides of the stem can present cement penetration problems later, but if your hull has a modern rounding off at the entry, over-lapping the stringers is probably inevitable. At the transom, overlaps are unlikely but if the stringer is cropped to length after it has been welded to the transom frame, a series of sharp protruding stubs will be the eventual result. A neater alter-native is to slip the inevitable chunk of waterpipe over the excess length of stringer immediately after welding while the metal is still red hot. The pipe is then used as a lever to turn the excess stringer through 90 degrees or so causing it to be-come part of the transom reinforcement. Even if not required in this role, bending the stringer thus and then cutting off the excess will ensure a much neater slightly radiused edge to the transom.

Maggie and I found that a welding session after clipping every dozen stringers to each side made for a reasonably varied work routine and the stiffness that even a dozen firmly fastened stringers impart to the hull basket is encouraging indeed. This is probably the reason that in no time at all, seemingly, we were clipping final stringers to the keel. By the time one is working in this region, the stringers should be running parallel to the keel bottom though if the hull has a lot of drag to the keel, it will probably be necessary to include a few short stringers in the deadwood region. These will enable the stringers beneath them to lie the straighter, acting like the stealer planks ('shooters' to the Cornish) in a conventional timber hull. At this stage, the skeleton of the hull is complete and though one can see the ghost of a boat there somewhere, the lack of substance is tantalizing when you stand back to take in your handiwork.

Similar frustrations occur when judging a good sheerline. If you use the same gauge of rod as the stringers to act as the sheerbar, you find that when you stand far enough away to see whether you have achieved a flowing curve, the rod is too thin to see. For this reason, if no other, Richard Hartley's idea of using $\frac{3}{4}$ by $\frac{1}{4}$-inch flat mild steel bar for the sheerline makes life a lot easier. The stiffness in the bar helps to avoid unsightly kinks and you can see it clearly from some distance after you have wired it temporarily in place. People building in confined spaces are really up against it at this stage. The first few feet aft of the stem head seem to be particularly vulnerable to hogging and sagging, and for this reason, if a boat must be built close to the wall of a building, make sure that at least the bow faces an open space.

You can judge the forebody sheer best by looking from positions from twenty to thirty feet away from the boat on the port and starboard bows. Closer in and directly ahead of her, with your eyes roughly level with the stemhead, the sheer bars will take on shapes like the bows in a ribbon and any unevenness should be easily apparent. Profile views will show up any unsightly junction between two lengths of bar:

a batten clamped along as much of their length as possible should enable you to smooth their meeting and they can even be welded into a continuous bar off the boat if need be. Quarter views at rail level are also good angles from which to make checks and adjustments. It is amazing how small a dip or hump the eye can detect: merely raising or lowering the sheer bar by $\frac{1}{8}$ inch can make all the difference between a shape in steel and a curve that sets the imagination tugging at its moorings.

Perhaps it is the importance of these small adjustments which has persuaded the amateurs of my acquaintance not to adopt ideas like those of Jay Benford's on sheerline construction. In some drawings I've seen, he suggests the use of quite substantial angle bent to shape for the amateur builder by the local engineering shop or suchlike. A personal view is that unless one is lucky in the engineer involved, the amateur builder has probably more notion of nice boat curves than he, and if the bar requires re-adjustment it must be difficult indeed to explain just what, where and how much is required. One might well end up accepting second best through sheer difficulty of communication. Maybe also, most ferro builders chose the medium for economy and too much work which must be contracted out to pros at pro's rates of pay must soon dissipate any savings.

Whichever sheer material you choose, may I recommend that before it is welded in place, you leave it tied in its final position for a couple of days while you work on something else. You sometimes notice more in a casual glance when your mind is miles from sheerlines than when you are studying the thing closely. It really is worth the little delay, for the sheer must be the boatiest line on the boat and it's my opinion that it is the dull gutless sheers of modern yachts that have created so many traditionally minded boatmen, not any amount of 'Tupperware'. When you are satisfied that your boat looks like a boat, weld the sheer bar to every frame, stem and stern.

At this stage, it might be as well to start applying mesh to the hull if your boat is a flush-decker with no large holes in the deck through which to man-handle large mesh panels. Equally those who have already opted for plywood decks may like to leap to the next chapter. The rest, however, will need to start clipping on the stringers for the deck. It seems that whether your deck stringers run parallel to the centre-line (like traditional workboat deck planks) or whether they are parallel to the deck edge (yacht fashion) is optional: perhaps it depends on how you were brought up. However, truly egalitarian ferro deck layers compromise by clipping the stringers near the centreline fore and aft and introducing progressively more curve as one works towards the deck edge. Generally, people seem to weld the ends of the stringers to the top edge of the sheer bar and clip—or tie—to the frames.

The simplest way with coachroofs seems to start by marking out the perimeter of the coachroof on the Overhead Datum Pipes, taking measurements from the centreline and the mid-section frame as necessary. From these overhead marks, it is an easy matter to drop plumblines to mark the coachroof shape on the deckbeams. The next step will be to weld—perhaps temporarily—vertical rods from deckbeams to the Overhead Datum Pipes. If the coachroof sides are to be of ferrocement, the designer should have provided an expanded drawing which will require lofting like the body plan, etc., and the rod framing welded up thereupon. If the coachroof sides are not to be raked inboard, they can be welded directly to or in place of the vertical rods. An inboard rake requires the cutting of timber wedges, wire-tied to the verticals before the coachroof side is located against them.

Easiest of all perhaps, is the plywood/timber coachroof which merely requires a substantial coaming to which it can be bolted. In this case, the vertical rods are simply used as uprights around which you work up the framework for the coaming. You may like to cut away these verticals after the coaming framing is complete—they are certainly going to be a nuisance while meshing—but if you leave them in place, they will provide valuable support for the sidedecks during plastering and when cut away afterwards, the stubs can be ground back and hidden under epoxy filler.

For smaller openings that also demand a coaming—hatches and the like—having tried building up the framework *in situ* on the boat and prefabricating coamings on the workbench, I now firmly recommend the latter course. It is not difficult to weld up the four sides of a rectangular coaming, web-frame fashion, and after drawing out that rectangle on chipboard, they can be held on edge with four blocks of wood suitably positioned. A few nails clenched over to hold everything steady, and then the corners can be welded. That way you are fairly sure of achieving a square-cornered frame with vertical sides which is not always the case when you fabricate the whole thing on the boat, said he, bitterly. The completed frame is then tied in position on the deck stringers and tack welded to each. The sections of the stringers in the way of the hatch are then cut away and the stubs ground back.

Openings that do not require flanges, whether on deck, in the house sides or the hull, demand much simpler framing. For ports, scuppers, fairleads, mast holes, etc., simple frames of mild steel bent to shape around home-made jigs and formers seem to be generally common. On plastering day, these openings are blocked off with appropriately shaped pieces of ply, wrapped in polythene so that they do not stick to the cement. However, the edges of all such openings are prone to voids in the cement around the rod framing, and doubtless the best way would be to cut holes afterwards in the finished hull. But thinking of the work that would be required in even one porthole seems good enough reason for accepting a few voids to be filled! Still, when you come to consider smaller holes for seacocks, etc., it is an alternative you might con-

sider; but do make yourself aware of the prodigious prices of
large masonry bits before you decide.

Finally, those ingenious systems for incorporating chain
plates, forestay attachment points and such into the steel
armature; I know of one designer who recommends that U-
shaped stirrups of stainless steel rod are welded to the armature to act as chain plates, for example, though I have yet to
see them in use. Obviously you make up your own mind
about how much is 'built in' to the ferro hull; my feeling is
that too many such features are a mistake. Though these fittings may be perfectly good initially, if your ferro hull lasts as
long as the experts say it should, wear and tear, stress and
strain is going to make its presence felt eventually. As Bruce
Bingham says, the theory that ferrocement continues to get
stronger with every year that passes does not take into account

19 Looking at the underside of the coachroof and foredeck on Luc
Delahaie's double-ender. Note framing for port and mast, scaffold
upright to transfer weight of building frame to cemented and supported keel, transverse rods to provide deck stiffening in way of mast.

the constant flexing and twisting which is the lot of any boat that gets used. Maybe unstressed areas increase their strength but it is the stressed areas that matter. Chain plates, for example. How on earth do you repair a rod chain plate that has worked loose within the armature without tearing off great areas of topsides? For this reason, I'm not alone in opting for as many bolt-on features on my cement boat as I would have if she were wood. Naturally, we'll have to make backing pads to take some of the load but if something goes wrong, years hence, we will always be able to drill fresh holes.

One more thing while I'm sermonizing and then I won't bore you further: if you are the sort of guy who builds his own boat then you are not likely to leave her alone once she is finished. Sooner or later, the creative urge will rear its ugly head: you'll wonder how she would go as a cutter, ketch, schooner or whatever. You'll think of a better place for the loo, galley or wall-to-wall stereo. Whatever it is, you are sure to want to alter it somehow: if all is irrevocably 'built-in' think of the frustrations. Keep it simple and keep it adaptable.

8

'. . . Creeps in this petty pace from day to day . . .'

Shakespeare: *Macbeth*

If you have not made up your mind already, now is the hour to decide between chicken wire and welded mesh and for once, it is a choice uninfluenced by costs—unless you know a fella who knows a fella who can get one type wholesale. You usually need that much more of the lighter 22-gauge chicken netting than the heavier 19-gauge welded mesh, so though you may get more square feet of chicken wire for your money, in this part of the world at least, costs are roughly equal.

As to the relative strengths of the two types, this is your designer's province and he should give categorical advice. In general, as ferrocement boats get smaller, designers are more likely to recommend welded mesh to enable a really thin hull skin to be achieved. Though steel is heavier than cement, it is usually the additional cement that makes a cement boat too heavy. Roughly speaking, four thicknesses of welded mesh are going to weigh around 1 lb per square foot and 6 thicknesses of chicken netting (the minimum recommended) will weigh around 12 oz per square foot, but when both are compacted and wire-tied around the same size stringers, the chicken netting lay-up will be that much thicker when plastered and that much heavier as a result. Perhaps for this reason, most of the amateurs I meet in Britain seem to be using welded mesh now—even, dare I say it, guys building Hartley designs where chicken netting is recommended: whether they obtained Mr H.'s approval, I know not.

Perhaps at this stage I can also mention a couple of varieties of mesh that I have yet to see in Britain. Aladdin Products of Wiscasset, Maine, USA, produce a heavy gauge 'mesh' in the form of long, thin planks which can be applied to the hull like double diagonal wood planking. Details of this 'Wire-Plank' can be found in Bruce Bingham's excellent book but too new to be included there is Aladdin's latest product, a 19-gauge ½-inch square mesh of high tensile wire that is woven, not welded. Called 'Str-r-etch' mesh, it is designed to do just that, enabling it to lie fairly over compound curves without all that dart cutting which we'll get to in a page or three. The British designer, Robert Tucker, tells me that he managed to obtain a similar product in Sharjah, United Arab Emirates, which was used on one of his designs with excellent results. Too late for my own use, I've also learned recently that N. Greening Ltd (PO Box 22, Britannia Works, Warrington WA5 5JX) produce a vast range of woven meshes in plain, tinned, galvanized, even stainless steel and in close consultation with your designer, you might like to consider their lists and specifications for Woven Wire Cloth and 'Agatex' high tensile steel screens.

However, since most will end up working with welded mesh, I'll concentrate on that henceforth, with the occasional walkabout for the chicken netting fancier, where relevant. As I've said, welded mesh comes in rolls 3 feet wide and 30 metres long (chicken netting—50 metres long), so perhaps the first step is to try to calculate the quantity you'll need. It's difficult because neither of us know how wasteful you'll be but to get a rough idea—and I do mean *rough*—try this:

Find the maximum distance from keel to sheer along the frame, in metres. Multiply this by a third of the boat length, in feet. Multiply again by twice your total number of mesh thicknesses and add *at least* 20 per cent for wastage, etc.

This figure will give you a notion of how many metres of mesh you'll want for the hull alone and does not allow for web frames, decks, coachroof, etc. Don't be afraid of over-buying: think of it as not so much a hedge as a fence against inflation. You can always sell any surplus to the legion who under-estimate and make a profit because you got maximum discount with a large order. Most important, you will not have to pay the (relatively) exotic amount forked out by the poor devil who trots back to the merchants for just one more roll!

Do shop around and collect as many estimates as possible before you buy. Get to the manufacturers if possible. If not, try steel suppliers, farm suppliers, gardening shops and so on. Whatever you do, don't forget to chat up the little iron-monger in the High Street who stocks one roll of mesh a year as a favour to the local Cage Bird Society. Many small traders these days are in bulk purchasing schemes and if he gets your large order, it may well 'promote' him to a better overall discount within the combine. Thus it can be worth his while to give you a very substantial discount. Of course, he'll naturally want cash on the nail and he won't appreciate his shop being clogged with twenty or thirty rolls of mesh for days before you collect. What precise discount you get will probably depend on mesh availability at the time and your brand of aftershave: a guide which may not still apply is that most of my friends managed between 25 and 33 per cent—and most of them have beards! As I said, it's worth shopping around.

To actually tie the mesh to the stringers, most seem to use plain soft steel wire between 1 and $1\frac{1}{2}$ mm in diameter. We used 1 mm which was probably a bit light but we managed: Brian Hancock got excellent results from $1\frac{1}{2}$-mm annealed stainless steel wire bought cheaply as motorway contract surplus. Again, buy in quantity: lots of dinky little coils in plastic bags from the DIY shop will come very expensive.

When you finally get around to wrestling with great chunks of wire netting, you have a variety of methods from which to choose. All have a distinctly Sam Peckinpah quality, however, so while you are convalescing from your antitetanus jab, I'll list a few modes of attack. Essentially, there are two areas of choice: the first is whether the mesh is applied in vertical strakes (Hartley), horizontal strakes (Benford) or diagonal strakes (Tucker). The second choice comes when you decide between applying each layer of mesh individually, or tying the lot together on the ground and applying them to the stringers as a mat.

As to choice one, all our local amateur builders adopted the Hartley system with the exception of Luc Delahaie but, of course, he's French . . . Despite our grim conjectures and working alone most of the time (we're a helpful lot, we Cornish ferrocement boatbuilders!), Luc made an excellent job of applying the welded mesh in long boat-length strakes following the instructions in Jay Benford's *Practical Ferrocement Boatbuilding*. The necessary tackles, etc., to do the job are all explained fully in the book and Luc proved to us sceptics that the system works. Nor were the scars he bore by plastering day any longer than ours.

If you too are a disbeliever, perhaps the Hartley way sounds simplest. In this system, all the panels are vertical with one layer overlapping another so that the edges do not coincide. Though the system is intended for chicken netting, it works as well with welded mesh, though if you tie the layers together off the boat the less tractable weld mesh can cause problems. The difficulty is that while several layers of chicken wire can be persuaded to take up compound curves, the rigid squares of the welded mesh make dart cutting necessary. Of course, this is no problem on the top layer of mesh but the inner ones are much more inaccessible. For this reason, and since in any case you may not be using more than two layers of mesh outside and two inside, may I recommend that you apply pre-tied mats only to areas of simple curves like the midship section. As you get to areas like the bow, put on one layer at a time: it is less hassle and probably works out quicker in the long run.

We did it this way. First we cut two lengths of welded mesh, using ordinary garden shears, about a foot oversize for the mid-section rail-to-keel distance. We then cut off a strip one foot wide from one of these pieces. This meant that when this strip was placed centrally on top of the other, there was a 6-inch overlap at each side of the bottom layer. When tying welded mesh together, Jay Benford recommends that squares of one layer are deliberately mis-aligned with squares of the other, producing in effect $\frac{1}{4}$-inch squares. He also encourages arranging the layers so that the finished mat is only 3 wire thicknesses thick (for full details of all this see *Practical Ferro-cement Boatbuilding*). We tried this with some success on these first midship panels but found it too difficult when we came to the super-bulbous bow of our *Spray*. Instead we concentrated on not superimposing one mesh pattern directly over the mesh beneath. With the mat tied with wire twists every 2 feet or so in both directions, it was ready to be fastened to the boat.

The initial location and attachment of large mesh panels to the hull is a fairly straightforward task for two people but an exercise in sheer masochism for one. Doing it the easy way, one person climbs inside the boat and locates him/herself on a plank across the LWL bearers. The chap on the outside—on staging or stepladder—then locates the panel against the hull with 6 inches of mesh projecting above the sheer bar. With a pocketful of tying wire cut into 4-inch lengths and bent into U-shapes, he pushes one of these staples through the mesh somewhere in the top central part of the panel, taking care that the staple does not go through both layers of mesh in such a way as to re-align them when twisted tight by matey inside. We'll assume that we are using pliers for wire twisting for the moment and look at speedier alternatives later in the chapter.

The next couple of ties should anchor the edges of the panel at the top and from there one works downwards, tying

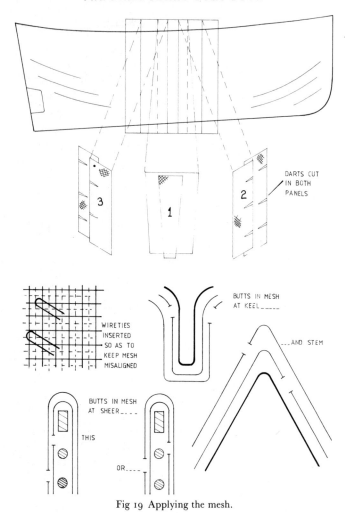

Fig 19 Applying the mesh.

to every—say—third stringer, always tying the centre of the panel first and smoothing out waves in the mesh as one progresses. I know that other builders tie less closely at this stage but they have that many more bulges to sort out later, so there is no time saved by it. Unless the boat is very small or very curvy, you should not need to cut darts (with garden shears or wire snips) on this panel.

A similar course is followed with the panels immediately fore and aft of this first panel though this time both layers are left full width and simply tied together with a 6-inch stagger or overlap to match up with the overlaps left on each side of the first panel. Darts in both layers will probably be needed on the forward edge of the forward panel and the after edge of after panel. Their number and their fiddliness will help you decide whether to start laying the mesh in single thicknesses yet. At this stage the mesh exerts little power of distortion on a securely suspended hull and you can finish off one side of the boat before starting on the other. However, this raises the point of what you do when the mesh layers from one side meet the mesh layers from t'other, whether under the keel or around the end posts. Well, what you *don't* do is overlap the lot so that in these areas you have twice as many thicknesses of mesh as you have in the rest of the boat. Sure, it ought to be stronger with all that extra steel there, but if you cannot get cement in and around all that steel because it is tied so densely, the resultant voids will only make the hull weaker— in the areas where you need all the strength you can get! Instead arrange all mesh joins anywhere in your ferro boat as you did on those first panels: that is with staggered butt joints in each layer so that while panels in the outer layer overlap joins in the inner layer, nowhere do you increase the number of layers of mesh in the hull. Brian's diagram suggests overlap patterns for keels and stems.

Meshing the inside of the hull will follow much the same pattern though the more cramped working conditions may inspire you to apply each layer singly from the start. On these concave curves, you have to work harder to get the mesh to lie tightly against the stringers which may mean even more ties and darts. Better to take out the bulges now, fiddling as it is, than hope you'll be able to sort it all later. You never can. Darts will also be needed to allow the mesh to run in and around the short bars in Perry-Sortun frames. With web frames, the layers of mesh have to be trimmed to lie snugly between the webs and it is here that a great deal of wastage can occur if the frames are spaced much closer than three feet.

It is generally accepted that in the area where the mesh covering a web frame overlaps on to the inside of the hull, it is OK to increase the number of layers of mesh. Perhaps the relatively flat areas involved make penetration easier and certainly web frames need fewer layers of mesh than the rest

20 Brian Hancock applies a twice-folded strake of chicken netting to a web frame.

of the hull. So instead of feathering the mesh on the frames into the mesh inside the hull, an easier system is used and to make things easier yet, many builders buy a roll or two of the more pliable chicken netting, just for the web frames.

For Hartley-style frames with a moulded depth of 3 inches, you simply cut a length as long as the half-frame and then fold it twice lengthways to make a panel 12 inches wide, three layers thick. This panel is then laid on the inner rod of the web frame and the centreline of the mesh panel is wire-tied thereto, with lots of extra ties in the turn of the bilge. With the panel really secure, timber wedges or even well-aimed feet are used to pummel the two flanges of mesh down each side of the frame, tightly into the corner and out along the hull. The mesh is then firmly tied to the web frame with ties to each stirrup and both rods. Tying down the flanges comes when we tie the whole of the hull basket and that comes next.

In case you have not heard, wire tying the whole of a ferro-cement hull basket has got to be the most tedious, time-consuming, thoroughly boring and absolutely vital task in the

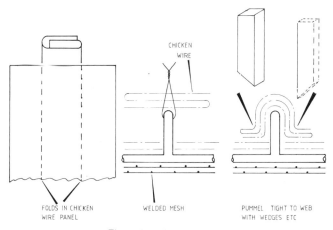

Fig 20 Meshing web frames.

21 If you must wire-tie single-handed, this 'crochet hook' is the Hartley way to tackle the job.

22 With someone else to push through the wire staples, the job is three times faster—and a lot less lonely.

whole of boatbuilding. The aim is to take out any bulges and ripples and tie it so tightly to the rods of the armature that the thickness of the rod and mesh sandwich is as thin as you can make it. The massive increase in rigidity that results will also help to maintain the hull shape when it is bombarded with cement on That Day. To achieve these aims means pushing a U-shaped wire-tie through the hull and twisting it tight at 2-inch intervals in every direction all over the hull. And that, neighbour, is a lot of pushing and a lot of twisting! Such a lot that it is most definitely a task for two people. One person can do it, using the crochet hook-type staple pusher described by Richard Hartley, and leaving all the wire twists on the outside of the hull to be bent back later. I did the whole of an 11-tonner this way, and that is why I say, without a doubt, it is a task for two people!

With one person outside to push staples and check on fairness and the other on the inside twisting the ends tight, it becomes just tolerable. But not then if the poor twister has to manage with ordinary tool-kit pliers. The pliers may do a good job of twisting and stand up well to constant use but

23 Pliers are only really recommended for wire-twisting in confined corners.

the twister's wrist won't—not even if he is a dart-playing pint drinker! Most ferro builders soon end up with an alternative wire twisting system.

On *Spray*, we used the idea of a Mini-Molewrench with a stub of rod welded to it that could be chucked into an electric drill. Full details appear in Jay Benford's book and when ours worked, it was both fast and effective. However, we found that constant wear and tear meant that the centreline of the wrench was being continually knocked out of alignment with the centreline of the drill: then it became a machine for

24 This Mini-Molewrench modified to fit in an electric drill is a much faster method but the two tools need careful alignment.

25 The same wrench chucked into a brace is slower
but stays true longer.

breaking wires. The same wrench used in a hand-drill or
brace seemed to stay true longer but, of course, work was
slower.

A variation of the molewrench we saw in use on a large
Hartley 'Fijian' seemed effective: the wrench had been
welded to the business end of a farmer's bag-tie puller so that
the wire-tie could be pulled tight and twisted simultaneously.
However, the common snag with most variations on the
wrench theme is the need for constant re-adjustment to keep

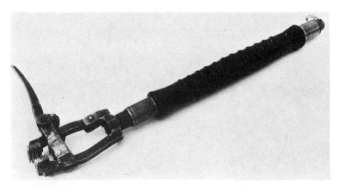

26 Jim Taylor of Newlyn devised this robust combination of a
farmer's bag-tie and a home-made clamp with a spring out of sight
between the jaws.

the things running sweetly. Another 'Fijian' builder, Robert Wilson of Redruth, used Jim Taylor's more business-like adaption of the farmer's bag-tie with the addition of a solid home-made clamp on the spring and cam principle. Sometimes it is suggested that the bag-tie puller could be used with —would you believe?—bag-ties but I have yet to meet anyone who has actually succeeded in getting the loops of the bag-ties through the holes in the mesh without compressing the loops so flat that they are unusable on the other side.

Certainly on our next ferro boat, we will follow the lead of Brian Hancock. Brian learned that all the nuts and bolts on those terrifyingly rattly bits on aeroplanes are additionally secured by a loop of wire, twisted tight and thus he tracked down the Rolls-Royce of wire-twisting devices: the 'Robinson Locking Wire Twister'. Available in 9-, 10- and 12-inch sizes, it's an industrial quality tool at a quality price (currently £14–£16) which, according to the manufacturers, Locktite UK Ltd, Watermead, Welwyn Garden City AL7 1JB, 'Grips the wires firmly, twists them to proper tightness and cuts neatly to complete the operation'. Certainly on Brian's 42-footer, we witnessed it performing all these tasks with ease.

27 Luxury wire-tying with the 'Robinson Locking Wire Twister'.

Another hull tying system, not using wire, was successful on a copy of Conor Cruise O'Brien's *Saiorse* built near Dartmouth. Here Steve and Jane Acester employed an industrial pneumatic stapler and a steel backing 'dolly'. With the dolly held firmly against the mesh on the inside of the boat, staples were fired from the other side so that the legs of the staple locked around a stringer. Apparently this method is not only effective but very fast indeed, but efforts by Luc Delahaie to use the same system himself slowed down somewhat when he learned the price of pneumatic staplers. However, if they are available for hire in your part of the world, it may be worth a few experiments.

Similarly in *Practical Boat Owner* magazine number 115, in an excellent article on ferrocement, David Waters gives tantalizing details of a wire-lacing method. Until I read this, I had subscribed to the general opinion that lacing could never hold the mesh as tightly as is needed. However, the author's *Pendragon* seemed such a superbly put together boat when she came into Falmouth in 1975, that I am sure the method might repay further investigation. Certainly lacing has its place as a way to tie down and together the adjacent edges of mesh panels so that they do not get pulled up by the plasterer's trowels; an idea I first saw on Crispin Rushworth-Lund's 48-footer.

Whichever method you choose, rest assured that progress will be slow: if you start the job thinking you'll be plastering in a couple of weeks, you'll be disappointed. Worse, you may rush the job and the only way to hide an insufficiently tied armature is to slap on lots of extra mortar: the worst thing possible for these smaller ferrocement hulls. Far better to expect the job to take an age and set a plastering date well into the future to give yourself time to tie, check for bulges and loose edges of mesh and tie again.

Also allow time for turning back all those ends of wire. Jay Benford's suggestion of a slotted screwdriver with which to grip the twist and roll the end over and back into the mesh works excellently, we found, but a large 10- or 12-inch screwdriver is less tiring to use than the one illustrated by Mr

28 Using a slotted screwdriver to turn back the ends of the twisted
wires into the mesh.

Benford. Certainly the alternative, using long-nosed electrical pliers, is slow by comparison with either. Of course, on
the first attack with the slotted screwdriver on the forest of
wire-ties in even the smallest ferrocement hull, there will be
some stray ends you miss. Some books say not to worry, you
can always chip them out and epoxy fill after plastering. Our
experience suggests that if you do this you will be chipping
and epoxying for the next three seasons at least. In the long
run, it is both quicker and cheaper to check the hull for the
wire-ties you have missed at this stage: the surest—and
bloodiest—way to find them is simply to stroke a bare hand
across the hull surface!

Gradually, as you find the last protruding wires and secure
the final loose edges of mesh, you may begin to experience a
visual pleasure in the material for the first time. Almost from
tree felling, the wooden boatbuilder has a joy in the patterns

29 Luc Delahaie taking his time over a thorough check for loose edges and projecting wire-ties.

and colours, even the feel and smell of his material, which is denied most emphatically to those who work in rusting rod and viciously barbed mesh. Now, when the mesh is so tightly compacted that the hull looks solid through half-closed eyes, you may find in the tracery of fine steel that, just for a while at least, ferro has a filigree beauty of its own. It almost seems a shame to hide it all under grey mortar. Take the last stages before plastering slowly and enjoy what you've built. If possible, find a friend with some photographic ability to do a photo survey; even if he cannot capture her beauty, the photos will be the only proof of the integrity of your workmanship if you ever want to sell her. You might, someday.

9

It ain't what you do . . .

Perhaps the only saving grace of thorough wire tying, apart from ensuring a light, fair hull, is the time it gives you to plan the final stages of the hull construction. There are several choices to be made and now you have the time to look closely at the various alternatives open to you. As I said, it is not the purpose of this book to tell you categorically how to build your boat but to describe some of the options open to you. There are three decisions to be made: which plastering technique?, which mix? and which plasterers to use it? I'll certainly try to give the information that helps you choose wisely but please supplement what follows by as much further reading, talking to other builders and most of all, participation in other people's plastering days as you possibly can: your choices will be all the better for it.

The good old-fashioned pipe-framed 40-foot dream machine was always plastered in one go, with a mob of extras like a de Mille movie. They carried buckets, not spears though and the only miracle was that they ever made the pubs before closing time. Nowadays, things are easier. Methods have evolved which require less muscle and fewer man-hours, especially on the smaller sort of boat. Both Jay Benford and Richard Hartley advocate sensible, well-tested plastering techniques and many amateurs have introduced their own variations of either method to suit their own needs and situation.

I suppose Jay Benford's way is nearest to the old way in that he still recommends that plastering be done in one day. Volunteers occupy the boat, spaced strategically on staging, and mortar is supplied to them by a bucket-carrying brigade. The mortar—'mud' he calls it—is pushed through the mesh by the volunteers and outside the boat the team of plasterers wait to float the emerging cement flush with the mesh. When mud has been pummelled into every crevice of the armature, the volunteers inside the boat scrape from the inside mesh all the surplus mortar: Jay Benford makes the point that any cement unreinforced with steel is just so much surplus weight. Hence the scraping which is followed by a stiff brooming, leaving the interior surface with a sort of welded mesh pattern 'Anaglypta' finish. When this is painted, it looks no worse than many a commercial resinglass interior you've seen and the surface is an excellent 'keying' base for the addition of cosmetic resin filler, where required. When the brooming is done, the volunteers leave the hull and after the cement has dried a little, the plasterers apply a thin outside coat which they trowel smooth and fair. Decks, if cement, have per-forated oil-treated pegboard wire-tied to the underside of the mesh to support the weight of the setting mortar which is vibrated down from above until it is seen emerging through the holes in the pegboard and the topside is floated smooth.

Richard Hartley, on the other hand, recommends the stage-by-stage approach to hull plastering devised by the New Zealand plasterer, E. R. Sayers. Far fewer volunteers are needed with this method since the hull skin is plastered in two shots. Volunteers bring mortar to the plastering team who use their floats to push cement into the outside layers of hull mesh and when this has dried somewhat, a second thin cosmetic coat is applied, faired and smoothed. After a 10- to 21-day curing period, the plastering team returns to tackle the inside of the hull mesh in the same fashion, having first grouted the inside face of the first layer of cement to assist bonding. Decks are plastered in the same two-shot manner, though a thin layer is applied to the underside of the deck in the first session to support the rest of the deck mortar, applied a fortnight later. Richard Hartley explains that though it would be bad practice to join old and new cement in building work, the rich mortars and dense reinforcements of ferrocement make cold joins perfectly safe.

These are the basic alternatives in technique, and doing a quick mental survey I think the amateur boatbuilders I know have favoured the Hartley technique to the Benford one by about two to one, perhaps because Hartley designs and systems are better known in Britain at the moment. The usual reason given, however, especially by those building larger boats, is that the Hartley way gives a longer time to the plasterers in which they can concentrate on a good finish. Equally those who have a little plastering ability say that it is not beyond the competent amateur to plaster the *inside* of a ferrocement boat, working carefully and doing perhaps one or two segments of a larger hull each day. Derek Blundell and his wife Sue did the inside of their Hartley 45 with no other help, for example, and the finished interior is excellent. Another point claimed by the Hartley' school is the fewer number of volunteers required with consequent savings on staging, buckets and other equipment and the general need for less battle planning beforehand.

The minority of us in the Benford camp locally are prepared to concede the virtues of the Hartley method on large boats without disagreement, I think. However, with boats under 30 feet, the advantages do not seem so obvious. Plaster can be pushed into the hull of the biggest 30-footer in around three hours, we've found, by as few as a dozen clued-up volunteers and this leaves plenty of time, even on a bad drying day, for the plasterers to get a good finish. Further, volunteers pushing mud by hand seem to be able to cope with a much drier mix than plasterers can push with floats: not only does this speed up the cement's 'going off', it's axiomatic that the less water there is in the mix, the less danger there is of shrinkage. Less than top-rate plastering teams are also less thorough in guarding against voids than interested volunteers, I've noticed, and the Benford way leaves the builder and his friends to concentrate on penetration and the plasterers to concentrate on the finish. Similarly, if you distrust your ability to float off the inside of the boat yourself, the Benford alternative is more economical than the extra expense of a second plastering day. Finally, the Benford way gets the whole business over and done with.

But straight away, I must add that decks are a different matter: I know of no-one who has actually tried the pegboard system: perhaps the cost of the boarding and the work in shaping it to fit the underside of the deck neatly is the deterrent. More likely is that the chance of the pegboard bellying downwards under the weight of all that cement with the danger of an overweight deck is a risk not to be contemplated and especially not on the smaller sort of ferro boat. Thus all the boats that I know have had their decks plastered by the two-shot system. First the underside, either trowelled to match the Hartley interior or brushed to match the Benford brushed finish on the hull and then the topside with plasterers to do the job properly.

This then is the first choice to be made, much influenced by your own circumstances and to a degree by your choice of plastering team: some crews have distinct preferences of their own. Whichever method you select, you will probably get a good result as long as your preparation and organization is efficient. Just how good depends on your plastering team, of course, and that is the next choice to be made.

Let me start by saying that there is a deal of difference between the results achieved by adequate plasterers and those achieved by good ones but this is nothing to the yawning chasm between the achievements of amateurs, even competent ones and any sort of professionals. DON'T, DON'T, DON'T consider doing it yourself or letting your brother-in-law, who did his own bathroom extension, anywhere near the job. I wish I could take anyone even idly toying with such a notion to look at a couple of neglected hulls I know in Yorkshire. One you would just not believe and the other, plastered by a bricklaying team (!), had more humps than a herd of camels. Get pros.

Which pros will depend on who is available and who you can afford. The first task is to get around the ferro boats of the district once again and discover just who plastered what. If you knew the fairness or otherwise of any of these before plastering, this will influence your judgment a great deal. For instance, if an armature which was as hilly as the Mendips sports a perfectly fair finish after plastering, don't touch that plastering team with a barge pole: the only way they could have achieved that result was by slapping on fill-in mortar by the barrowload! Better a bumpy hull that floats any day. If you live inland, it may well be worth your while to point the annual holiday in the direction of some boaty area where cement boats—and good plastering teams—are thicker on the ground, just so you get to see what the best crews can achieve. You may even decide to pay such a team to travel to your site and put them up overnight: if they are good, it might well be worth it.

Your team will have their own ideas and it is well worth listening to what they have to say. If it sounds sense, fine, but bear in mind that some plasterers know far more about getting a good finish than about ferrocement boatbuilding and the necessity for total penetration of the armature. It is worth taking trouble to find a crew who will do the job the way you want it done. They may make suggestions as to the number of plasterers your boat will need, for instance and strangely, they sometimes underestimate. A minimum of two plasterers for all but the tiniest ferrocement hull would seem advisable from my experience; four would not be too many for a 30-footer and a fifth might not come amiss. On the day, such a number might seem to be having a very easy time of it for the first few hours but at the finishing-off stage, all will be busy. As someone very involved with building boats as cheaply as possible, I really do feel that one area where it is folly to economize is in the quantity and quality of your plasterers.

One area where you might consider economy, for example, is in the mix itself. I do know that many amateurs 'up-country' have used the pre-mixed and bagged Rendaflor Yacht Mortar from MacAlister Carvall of New Milton, Hampshire, with entirely satisfactory results. The mix consists of ordinary Portland cement and selected, graded sharp sands in 25-kg sacks, and the manufacturers claim that not only is the mix especially easy to use on site but that it also allows good workability with the minimum water content. Ian Wright of Ilford used this pre-bagged mix on his 27-foot Hartley 'Tasman' and found the pre-measured quantities particularly handy on plastering day.

However, the relative costs of the pre-bagged mortar and a home-brewed mix of local sand and cement deserve consideration. Inevitably prices may have risen by the time you read this but as a rough guide, the following figures might be useful. At the time of writing, RF Yacht Mortar costs £59.50 per tonne (that's 0·98 of an old-fashioned ton) and at my local builders' merchants, not known for price cutting, Portland cement costs £40 per ton and good sharp plastering sand costs £7 per ton. Thus a locally bought 2 to 1 mix would cost £18 per ton, plus local delivery charges, against, say, £60 per ton for Yacht Mortar, plus delivery from Hampshire. Thus in 1977, Tim Hurst of Bursledon, building a Benford 35-foot double-ender, had a bill for £450 for pre-bagged yacht mortar while Luc Delahaie, plastering a slightly larger double-ender at the same time, paid about £100 for a local mix. You may well decide that the quantities involved in the smaller sort of ferrocement boat, the convenience on plastering day and the security of a Lloyds

Approved product makes that additional expense worthwhile, however.

Having said that, I must record that by far the majority of the impecunious ferrocement boatbuilders that are my acquaintances elected to make up their own mix from locally available sands and cement. One or two followed the rather elaborate instructions for choosing sands given in Cairncross's *Ferrocement Yacht Construction* but most of us seem to have based our selection on the far more practical advice of Hartley or Benford and the first-hand experience of local amateurs and plasterers.

At its simplest, Benford and Hartley agree that you need a sharp plasterers' sand; in effect, a fine aggregate of crushed rock or stone with its strength undiminished by the presence of mud, lime, shell, coral or other organic matter. Some impurities can be got rid of by hosing with fresh water and the salt in beach sand must also be removed this way. Richard Hartley suggests that sand can also be graded during the washing process by hosing it through a $\frac{1}{8}$-inch sieve, any larger particles being discarded. Equally the sand must not be too fine or the mix will absorb a great deal of water with the danger of loss of strength and shrinkage cracks later on; thus, only around 30 per cent of the sand should pass through a $\frac{1}{32}$-inch sieve.

By talking to your plasterers about the local sands, it is possible to relate this advice to what's available. Derek Blundell's solution was to mix two Cornish sands in equal parts: one part washed Gwithian beach sand and one part Blue Elvan from the Newlyn granite quarries. Mike Robson, working in Yorkshire, found that Doncaster sand on its own was perfectly suitable. However, if you are concerned that your mix be of maximum strength and wish to go for a properly 'engineered' mixture of different-sized sand particles, you can do no better than consult Jay Benford and Herman Husen's *Practical Ferrocement Boatbuilding*. Similarly, if you have doubts about the presence of impurities in your sands, having tried the basic test of shaking a handful in a jamjar of water and waiting for the sediment (the impurities) to collect over the sand, professional advice should be sought either from the designer or the Cement and Concrete Association Information Division, 52 Grosvenor Gardens, London SW1W OAQ (01–235 6661).

The cement most used in the cement boats I've seen has been conventional Portland cement (US Type 1) though one or two richer souls did spend the few extra pennies on sulphate-resisting cement (US Type 5) in the hope of better resistance to the sulphates in sea water. Perhaps in an effort to keep things simple and maybe also because of the on-going debate among authorities on ferrocement as to their value, most of us seem to have kept additives to a minimum; though I understand that one or two added various percentages of pozzolan for better workability of the mortar with less water. Similarly, in Britain, where galvanized meshes for ferro-cement boatbuilding seem to be the unfortunate norm, the designer may be concerned about the interaction between the zinc on the mesh and the lime in the cement resulting in hydrogen bubble voids in the hull and may suggest the addition of chromium tri-oxide. However, I've yet to find any published material available to the average home boat-builder on just how much of the stuff to add to a mix: if your designer is able to give precise and expert guidance, fine; if not, it is another additive I would leave alone.

As to the sand–cement ratio, for once there seems to be an unusually happy consensus that the best mix for a ferro-cement boat lies between *1½ parts sand to 1 part cement* and *2 parts sand to 1 part cement*, parts incidentally by weight or volume. The relatively high cement content, compared with the goo that brother-in-law used on his bathroom, is there for strength and imperviousness basically, though it does make the cement rather brittle. Thus less than 1½ parts of sand is going to make the hull too brittle, despite all that mesh; but with over 2 parts of sand porosity may be a problem, as will be the reduced chance of getting a good surface finish. As Robin Benford puts it, the cement is the glue that sticks together the sand: too much glue and the joint is weak, too little and it's the same. Thus great fence sitters, like the Greenfields, have opted for a $1\frac{3}{4}$ parts sand to 1 part cement ratio but many other amateurs decide to save money and go for 2 : 1.

That leaves the water in the mix and I think I've already flogged the point that to ensure maximum strength and minimum shrinkage the mix should have the minimum water content consistent with workability. As to how you measure that quantity is such an empirical problem that we will leave the topic until the description of plastering day. As to the kind of water, one word will answer: pure. Sea water is useless and so is the stuff from the stream behind the chemical defoliant factory; if in doubt, have it tested.

10

'Now entertain conjecture of a time . . .'

Shakespeare: *Henry V*

In the weeks before and after plastering the keel—a sort of rehearsal (see Chapter 11)—you'll find plenty to keep you busy and perhaps your first task will be to fix a definite date for the main plastering job—the hull proper. Obviously this is going to be governed by the availability of your plastering team and that probably means you'll be restricted to week-ends. Since your volunteer labour force is also more likely to be free then, this is no bad thing. Saturday generally ends up as the day chosen and there's the advantage here that the shops will be open if there is any item you've forgotten.

Having fixed a day, let everyone involved know about it now. Let the hire firm know that you will require two mixers, ideally the plasterers' paddle type if they have them. More likely, you will have to make do with the revolving drum type but most people seem to get by. It might well be that the second mixer remains a spare in case the first breaks down but if your hire firm has sent you one duff mixer, it's probably sent two! If you have a friend who loves these small petrol or diesel engines—even if he loves not cement boats—persuade him to come down that Saturday morning, just in case. You may also like to hire a vibrator just in case you need one but the type that most firms supply, a poker 18 inches long and as thick as a broomstick, can shake out just as much mortar as it shakes in. Give this obvious phallic symbol to some *machismo*-besotted twit and he could ruin everyone's efforts in minutes: if you must use one, give it to someone sensible with nothing to prove.

This is also the time to secure solemn oaths from friends who are to help that they will indeed turn up on the day, on time. Take some trouble to let them know what they are in for: what clothing to wear, how long they will be needed and if possible at this stage, what job they will do. A leisurely explanation in a disco-less pub a couple of weeks in advance is infinitely preferable to hastily screamed instructions over the racket of two mixers on plastering day: get them involved now and they may have some sensible pertinent suggestions to make. The more interested your volunteers become, the more likely are they to do a conscientious job on the day: treat them like unpaid muscle and that is all you'll get. Be careful also that too many are not involved: one person to take photographs is great, three . . . and the man from the local paper . . . and friends from the drama group or darts team or Brownies . . . and some friends that the dog's made and you have a recipe for absolute chaos!

Having decided on your plastering technique, you should be able to work out how many assistants will be needed and also what staging, access to the boat, etc., they will need. The firm that supplied the scaffolding of the building frame will also be able to rent you the extra lengths and boards for the staging around the boat. If possible, set up a double plank walkway all around the hull at a height which enables the plasterers to reach the highest part of the sheerline comfortably. Take some trouble to see that these boards do not slip on the steel piping by nailing locating blocks to the undersides, where necessary. If you have decided to adopt the Hartley 'two-shot' plastering technique, you can also arrange your staging to positively discourage anyone, especially that keen photographer, from climbing inside the boat while the plasterers are floating her off. Have a private route of your own, maybe but keep the rest out.

With the Benford 'one-shot' technique, safe and easy access to the interior for volunteers and mortar and adequate staging once there is essential. Do think very carefully about the logistics of this operation. When you have erected a system of ladders (I know one guy who used an old house staircase) and of internal walkways, try walking the whole system yourself with a bucket of water or sand half a dozen times. Staging that appears quite safe and steady when you have both hands free can suddenly become very hairy when you are carrying heavy buckets.

Such a test might encourage you to think of alternative methods of getting the cement to the volunteers inside the boat. Your first thought may be a good seamanlike tackle but these things are difficult to locate: it has to be far enough from the hull so as not to interfere with the work of the plasterers and yet near enough so that a full bucket can be lifted inboard: a bucket of mortar at arm's length is no light thing and one dropped could do considerable damage to the boat —or worse. I know one builder who hired a fork-lift truck for plastering day: with a pallet as a platform, several buckets at a time could be lifted quickly to the right level and driven inwards to make removal and distribution of the mix easy. Some hire firms can supply miniature versions of the very basic lifts (elevators) they use on building sites which might be used. Whichever system you fancy, give yourself time to test it properly beforehand: everyone will do a far better job on the boat if they are not working extra hard to make up for deficiencies in your planning or worrying about their safety because of deficiencies in your staging.

One system I've read about but never seen used is the 'Gunnite' mortar pump. I get the impression that the mortar has to be rather sloppy to make it pumpable and that would immediately rule out the method. However, I am sure that someone sooner or later will invent a means of getting good stiff mortar where it's needed and when they do, it may well be worth using—after the other guy has tried it on his boat first.

138

As with all kinds of planning, it is simply a choice of alternatives using as much wisdom and foresight as you can muster. How much wisdom you find out on plastering day. For example, you have to choose where to store your sand: too near the boat and the piles get in the way or worse, sand gets blown over the setting cement; too far and your volunteers will walk miles. Whatever you do, cover over the piles until the day: sand soup laced with doggie piddle is not the best of boatbuilding materials. You have a similar choice as to where you locate your mixing area: not too far from the mix components, of course, or so close to the action that no one can hear themselves think.

It is also a good moment to consider a choice you may have to make at the start of plastering day: in Apollo parlance, the 'Go/No-Go'. What will you do if the heavens open, carry on regardless or call it off? I helped shove mud on a ferro boat that was plastered in a Cornish shower, a downpour that was coming back out of the drains within minutes and caught the poor boatbuilder completely unprepared. His sands and mixer were all out in the open and the man on the mixer had been thoroughly bulled up beforehand on how hard he would have to work to make lots of mix. Work hard he did, producing bucket after bucket to stand until the pushers needed it and as a result . . . well, have you ever tried to push mushroom soup? Moral: be prepared to call the whole deal off until a better day or be prepared to face the stimulating variety of the British climate. It is not that difficult to rig up a temporary shelter over the mixing area at least.

Perhaps the worst goof of all on this particular plastering day was the way that the builder in question was setting an excellent example to his mud pushers by being in the boat the whole time, getting really stuck in, pushing harder than anyone. As a result, there was no one to make any decisions, organize other volunteers, control the flow of mix, answer stupid questions, deter onlookers from getting aboard, etc.,

etc., etc. Please, much as you might fancy working out the anxieties of the day in some simple therapeutic task, don't. The builder owes it to the volunteers to leave himself available to sort out any difficulties that beset them. The builder must be able to move around, see everything and generally control the whole operation. Don't get me wrong, I am not suggesting for a moment that you let rip on your Napoleonic tendencies and put everyone's backs up: simply be there, everywhere, to help and advise. Someone has to do it. It ought to be the one who knows most about the job. You.

Now is a good time to prepare for that role by listing everything you will need on the day while you still have time to gather the things together. With mixers and materials on order, what about water for the mix? If it's on tap, great; if not, start collecting and cleaning old oil drums or domestic water tanks. You'll have to fill them by bucketing good water from somewhere. Check that you have sufficient buckets for plastering day at the same time: two or three for the mixing crew, one for each mud-pusher (one-shot) or each plasterer (two-shot) and at least a couple in transit. You might well borrow some of them from ferro builders who have already plastered. Galvanized steel ones are best if you have any choice: the plastic sort split and the rubber ones like to shed their handles, usually under load! The mixing crew will also need a couple of shovels, sand measuring boxes if the mix proportion is tricky, spare fuel and maybe also a spark plug for the mixers. Volunteers will require industrial-type rubber gloves (Government surplus stores are a cheap source) and for one-shotters, hand-sized quadrilaterals of plywood to scrape surplus mortar from the interior and some stiff brooms for the final brushing. What you won't need are plasterer's floats: the volunteers will do a far better penetration job with their hands and we found that scraping with ply is far less likely to claw out cement already enmeshed. The plasterers will have their own, of course, but what they may not bring are 'derbies': thin springy battens of 1 by $\frac{1}{4}$-inch timber, about 3–4 feet long, with blocks at each end as handles. After the first floating, the plasterers will use these to fair up the hull, removing surplus plaster and revealing hollows as they progress. They might need derbies making, so check. They may also expect you to supply sponges for the final finish.

Another section of your Super Master List might deal with food and drink, especially if some items need advance ordering. Food of the kind that can be consumed on the trot is best: sausage rolls, doughnuts . . . you know the sort of thing. It's also thirsty work: add to the list a camping stove and paper cups for lots of coffee. As the temperature climbs, they'll need something wetter: cans of beer, lager, etc. However, where booze is concerned I would err on the mean side: of course, you must replace all that's lost in honest sweat but if the party atmosphere creeps in your boat will suffer. It shouldn't be a mad night at the Mardi Gras or a booze-up in Blackpool: settle for a couple of beers. If you feel you have debts to pay to your helpers, why not wine and dine them royally— afterwards.

Perhaps the final section of The List could be headed 'Jobs to do before . . .' I've already mentioned making measuring boxes and derbies but there are other equally essential exercises in primitive woodwork. Working from deck level downwards, the first requirement is a batten around the sheerline. Good old knot-free pine perhaps 1 or $1\frac{1}{2}$ inches by $\frac{3}{8}$ to $\frac{3}{4}$ inches, wired on edge to the hanging rods and the sheer bar enables the plasterers to get a good edge to the sheer. For the same reason, any openings in the hull for ports, scuppers, seacocks, etc., will need to be blanked off with ply which has been either well sanded and sealed at the edges or covered in polythene sheet: any edge roughness will provide a key for the cement that could cause chipping and flaking of the hull when the blanks are removed. Estimate how thin a layer of cement will cover the mesh and have your ply blanks thick enough to stand proud of the surrounding mesh by just this amount. If the ply stands out too much, there's a tendency for mortar build-up around them, leaving Hawaiian-type volcanoes when the blanks are removed. Likewise, if the blanks are too thin, the plasterers will plaster right over them, meaning lots of chipped nasty edges when the blank is removed—if you can ever find it.

Hardly woodwork, but if you decide to have a bolt-on keel below the cement one, you will probably need holes for the bolts running across the keel (i.e. horizontal not vertical). Since drilling through 8 inches of ferro isn't on, use dowel pegs now to make the bolt holes. Similarly, if you have already made your lower rudder pintle, use this to locate the dowel pegs for the bolt holes that will also be needed here.

And while we are hole making: once the water cure begins, the hull will soon start to fill up with water and the pressure could severely distort the green cement. Thus it is a good idea to attach to the mesh some small ply scraps, 2 inches in diameter or so, in each of the web floors if they are to be plastered at the same time as the hull and in the hull-skin itself, as low down as practicable. There will need to be a piece at each side of the mesh, of course—the two are wired together like back-to-back buttons—and they are all removed just before the cure begins, to allow the water to drain away.

An idea from Richard Hartley that we used successfully on our web-frame boat is the tying of timber battens to the inside edges of the web frames, both on the hull and under the decks, like internal ribbands. On the hull, the mid-area between each frame is then given additional support by wiring the mesh to the batten with a loop of hefty wire. Under the deck, where the batten is below rather than above the mesh, a polythene-wrapped woodblock of suitable size is forced between the batten and the mesh above, again to provide support mid-way between frames. Of course, when the cure is over, there will be indentations left on the underside of the deck and on the web frames but these are easily filled with resin filler.

Three jobs remain: one optional and two vital. To take the optional one first, most books seem to tiptoe around the matter of installing the stern tube, and give scant guidance at best. Perhaps you'll get more help from the designer's drawings. If not, it may be of interest to know how a couple of other amateurs and ourselves approached, rather than solved, the problem. To us, the notion of casting in a tube whose precise and accurate location is essential, amid the onslaught of several tons of mortar, not to mention the pounding of numerous fists, seemed—and still seems—to be inviting trouble. Thus we decided that whatever plastering technique was to be employed on the rest of the hull, the vicinity of the stern-tube would be done by the two-shot method with the area of mesh inside the hull left bare of plaster so that the tube could be set up carefully and plastered in leisurely on another quieter plastering day all of its own. In fact, all three of us left this plastering session until fitting out was well advanced and engine installation was being tackled. Thus in the preparations for the first plastering day, the only task was to mask off the interior of the stern-tube nacelle with polythene and masking tape so that the area remained free and unsplattered.

Of the two vital tasks, one does not take more than a few minutes. When that boat of yours is plastered, all those neat little paint marks on the frames which indicate the LWL will be obliterated, of course. Thus it is necessary to get the transparent hose out once again, or tape a spirit level to a long straight edge, in order to transfer a mark at LWL level to some permanent looking structure nearby. Don't use the building scaffold, it should not happen but there may be some slight subsidence during plastering: use a wall instead so that archaeologists years hence can essay wildly at the social significance of your novel graffiti.

And so, chaps, to the last task of the plastering day preparations and the most vital of the lot. Leave lots of time for it and if necessary, postpone plastering.

The faster concrete dries, the more it shrinks. If you walked away and left the hull after plastering, in a few days it would be a mass of shrinkage cracks. Worse, you would lose out on the phenomenal strength increase which is gained by prolonging the chemical interaction between cement and water. Thus all ferrocement hulls should be kept wet as long as possible after plastering and not allowed to dry out even slightly. The practical minimum for this 'curing' period is around ten days but many builders like to prolong the cure up to twenty-eight days: after that the cement is apparently capable of maintaining the chemical strengthening process without further wetting.

So that's your problem: keeping the brute wet, and wet continuously; if she dries out once, subsequent wetting is pointless. Thus hosing her down before you go to work in the morning and when you come home in the evening is unlikely to work even in the wet West of England. With a rota of volunteers who will come and hose the boat while you are out, you may get by just as long as everyone understands the essential nature of their own contribution. Ian Wright cured his 27-foot Hartley 'Tasman' for 21 days, hosing her down at 8.00, 12.00, 5.00, 7.00 and 9.00 each day, having first ensured that the hull was protected from drying winds by an all-over polythene tent.

Most builders tend towards some continuous automatic wetting process, however. Most common is a perforated hose strung around the sheerline. The easiest way seems to tie the hose to the edging batten so that it can be set up and tested before you plaster without it being in the way on the day. Thorough testing is absolutely essential to determine the adequacy of the water pressure, correct size and number of holes and whether the system can run for hours on end without clogging. Water pressure and hole size are directly related: if your boat has any sort of a sheer about her and the holes in the hose are too large, you get steady streams of water amidships and nothing at the ends. If the holes are small and water pressure adequate, you get water from every hole in the system and better still, those fine sprays of some force are much more effective in wetting large areas. One builder I know coupled hoses from two yard taps to a manifold fabricated from plastic water pipe T-junctions in order to maintain pressure: Lord knows what his water bill was like! Actual hole sizes and spacing must be determined by experiment: we found that $\frac{1}{32}$-inch holes at 4-inch spacings worked well but don't take our word, test it. Incidentally, due to the perverse shapes of boats, some areas are more prone to drying out than others—parts of the transom, run and deadwood, for example—and you may need more closely spaced holes in the hose in these regions. Of course, you can always make extra holes after plastering if necessary, as it is extremely difficult to see whether anything as insubstantial as a ferro boat basket is being wetted uniformly. Far easier to test, and really more important, is whether the system you've cobbled together is actually going to run continuously for as long as it's needed. The only way is to try it beforehand and see: it may help get rid of all the decaying leaves, flaking zinc, etc., trapped in the armature. Incidentally, holes in the hose that have been prodded, not drilled, tend to clog after an hour or two, you'll find.

If, like me, you are concerned with the enormous wastage of an important resource like water in the curing of even a small ferro boat, you may like to give some thought to some alternatives to the mains connected system. Unfortunately, our own efforts to recirculate the curing water from a dug-out polythene-lined holding tank under the boat by means of a bilge pump were none too successful: the pump was not man enough and grit washed off the hull got into the hose and clogged the holes. With a more powerful pump and a deeper, narrower holding tank to allow the sand to settle, you might be more successful. Paul and Fae Miller, writing in Benford Newsletter 1/9, described such a system with a top-up refinement from the mains which used a toilet cistern float valve where the mains hose entered the tank. However, I learned from the Cement & Concrete Association that after an initial cure of two or three days with fresh water, it would have been perfectly safe to continue the cure with sea water pumped ashore: if circumstances suit, you might like to try this instead.

You might also give some thought to the use of a curing membrane of the sort used on airport runways, etc. Sealo-crete Group Sales Ltd make several: the resinous type being most efficient but leaving paint adhesion problems as a possibility later. Sealocure Curing Aid LR/B20 is not a membrane but a layer of crystals which retard evaporation and may well be worth investigating; especially if you can track down ferro builders with direct experience of its use. However, Sealo-crete Ltd do recommend the use of additional protection from the sun and wind and even then 'slight surface crazing' might be possible.

Whichever curing system you choose, you'll need to buy polythene sheet or hire tarpaulins or both for it is absolutely vital to protect the curing hull from those 'good drying days' that were all the rage before they invented spin driers. Your wife will tell you it is not the sun that dries out your long johns on the line but the wind, and it is the wind that's so hard to keep out. Polythene nailed over wood frames which are then lashed to the top and sides of the scaffold frame can be effective if it does not have to withstand the Cornish brand of gale but as soon as one tear starts, it is not long before the whole panel gets blown out. One solution to this is to protect the polythene in turn with hired tarpaulins but that sounds somewhat expensive.

Far more effective and less vulnerable, is to wrap the hull, rather than the scaffolding, in a polythene winding sheet using the heavy gauge builders' polythene that comes in 12-foot wide rolls. Of course, you'll have to postpone this task until after plastering but a generous amount of polythene will have to be bought now and lots of old rope scrounged for parcelling her up.

An afterthought in our plastering day preparations (and in this chapter!) was to make up a one-foot square sandwich of rod and mesh identical to the hull skin. Plastered on the day, it provided an easy means of working out the finished hull weight and could also have been used to determine hull strength and the efficiency of the cure. If a local technical establishment would help, slabs could be made up and cured with the hull; one panel being sent for compressive strength testing after each week of the cure.

That about does it: do take your preparations slowly and make them as thorough as you know how. In the hullaballoo of plastering, it is frequently impossible to 'sort something out' that should have been better prepared. Do it now while you have time to think. If there isn't time, make time; postpone plastering if need be. Don't plaster that boat until you are good and ready.

Recent Developments in Dry Curing
Since all the foregoing was written, Brian Hancock's 42-foot ketch and the two 28-foot working boats building locally have been plastered. Not one of the three used a conventional water cure. Instead, they used Unibond Limited's 'HydrEpoxy 300': a water-based epoxy water-proofing agent which can be applied to damp cement. Each boat was painted with two coats of the sealant on the day after the hull was plastered and no further effort was needed to keep the outside of the boat wet. The deck framing was then covered over with polythene to inhibit evaporation inside

the boat and as a 'belt and braces' precaution, the interior was damped down with a watering can every couple of days or so.

Initial impressions are that the process is a great deal easier than the most trouble-free water cure, is no more expensive since 'HydrEpoxy 300' is an excellent epoxy priming coat for the hull and, most important, all three hulls appear to have cured properly. The process was given considerable testing by Samson Marine (Bridgend Quay, Newton Ferrers, S. Devon) before it was used locally, and independent tests at a laboratory have determined that cement blocks cured with 'HydrEpoxy 300' have a compressive strength of 8,300 lb per sq inch as against 10,000 lb p.s.i. for blocks given a conventional water cure; both figures being obtained after a 28-day curing period. While 'HydrEpoxy 300' is not quite so effective as a good laboratory water cure then, it should be noted that it still exceeds the minimum strength requirements quoted by Richard Hartley (5,600 lb p.s.i.) and just gets above the Jay Benford minimum (8,000 lb p.s.i.).

Further details from:
Unibond Limited, Tuscan Way, Industrial Estate,
Camberley, Surrey GU15 3DD.

II

Floating cement

Well, you finally got here and it will not have escaped your notice that this boat-shaped basket of yours is still hovering off the ground like an overweight dirigible. Now in good old-fashioned cement boatbuilding, we would have blocked up that keel from the start and not bothered to suspend her, laughed at the consequent difficulties of meshing under the keel and left the underside devoid of plaster on plastering day, saving for ourselves the treat of attempting to back-plaster the thing while the crane swings her aloft on launching day. And if all that sounds a touch bitter, guess which amateur cement boatbuilder did it the old-fashioned way . . .

Since then I've seen it done the easy way. The suspension system described earlier is more than capable of taking the extra weight of an inch or so of mortar along the bottom of the keel and the job is an unhurried 'dry-run' for plastering day proper. There is no need for fancy organization: all you'll need is a mixer, a volunteer or two and a small quantity of your chosen mix. What you do is to push and pound (vibrate if you must) an inch or so of mortar down into the rods and mesh at the bottom of the keel. Naturally, when every crevice has been filled, the mortar will start to ooze out through the mesh at the bottom and then the volunteer who is least frightened of a plasterer's float, skims the underside of the keel with a protective layer of around $\frac{1}{4}$ inch of mortar. The sides of this one-inch layer are best brushed back hard with a stiff brush, baring plenty of mesh to provide a key for the cement of the rest of the hull. Primed with Unibond or Epoxy Concrete Adhesive, the join is no problem.

Curing the keel needs nothing too fancy either: a pile of water-soaked blankets, sacking or other old cloth, strung out along the top of the cement and watered regularly will probably suffice. After one or two weeks of curing, you will be ready to shore her up: all but a fraction of the weight of the boat will be on the keel blocks thereafter so make them good. We used a mixture of breeze blocks (on edge; the lowest ones in piles laid flat have been known to disintegrate) cemented to primitive foundations and finally chocking up securely with assorted pieces of timber but not so securely as to lift the armature. Of course, the entire plinths could be timber, old railway sleepers and the like, but do err on the side of too many rather than too few: one every three or four feet isn't overdoing it. When she is secure, you are ready for The Day.

Down on the site, about a half-hour before the volunteers arrive, you can start getting things ready. Get out mixers, measuring boxes, shovels and buckets. Make sure that the mixing water is to hand, wheel out the bags of cement from the dry storage and uncover your sand pile. Set up the coffee and snacks area away from the mainstream of activity, perhaps in the back of a van or boot of a car. Direct the volunteers to park their own transport well out of range of cement splatter and allot them specific tasks if you have not done so already. Each volunteer will need a pair of rubber gloves, remember, and if anyone has arrived unsuitably dressed in cavalry twills and chukka boots, warn them now of what's to follow.

You cannot start mixing until your plastering crew arrives: cars have been known to break down or they may have got the date wrong! While you are waiting, give all the staging and ladders a final safety check.

Once the gang are here, it's all go. The sensible type you have chosen to lead the mixing crew starts up the mixer and pours in a small quantity of water and then adds the sand or sands and lets them turn over a while. Then comes the measured quantity of cement and then water is added very slowly, a little at a time until the mix is as dry as can reasonably be worked. The first mix, while you are learning, may well be too sloppy: dump it, don't make do. As a guide, the mix should be stiff enough to stand easily in piles without sagging. One-shot plastering schemes seem to make a better, slightly drier mix possible. This is because the volunteers can force it into the mesh with gloved hands whereas the plasterer's float seems to distribute his pushing power too widely.

Before the first bucket of mud is pushed into the hull, one volunteer quickly primes the keel sides with mortar adhesive, such as Unibond or Sealocrete's 'Epoxy Tack Coat and Adhesive'. Then two-shot plasterers, working outside the boat, will use sweeping upward strokes to force the plaster into the first layers of mesh. In the thin armatures of smaller ferro boats, penetration will be easy so the builder might well decide to use that private route round into the hull. If your plasterers don't know their own strength or they have been used to the denser structures of fifty-footers, they may be pushing mortar right through the armature, leaving you a million concrete nipples to chip away before you can plaster the interior. If so, have a quiet word: she is still your boat.

With the one-shot, each volunteer in the boat has a bucket of mud. Working from the keel upwards and inwards from stem and stern, they force mortar right through the mesh, paying special attention to any angles in web-frames, posts, etc., and to the perimeters where their own patch meets the next man's. My own favourite mud-pushing technique is a combination of throwing handfuls hard at difficult corners and slapping with the flat of the hand in easier areas. It is a little difficult at first because the mesh appears to bounce the stuff right back at you but eventually a technique is evolved. Half an hour in, and everyone should be steaming along nicely; the builder may even have the second mixer started to keep up the flow and at this stage also, mixing mistakes can occur so the builder will maintain an unobtrusive watch on mix quality.

Even though the one-shot method must be slower because the entire thickness of the mesh has to be penetrated, you will still be surprised, I think, how quickly you are the owner of a cement boat. Sonny and Kathy Wieck's 18-footer had this stage over in only 45 minutes. Even our 33-foot 11-tonner was fully penetrated in 3 hours, deep floors and all. By early midday, if not long before and whichever method you adopt, the mixers will be turned off and the plasterers, having roughly floated the top surface, will be waiting for the mortar to 'go off' sufficiently to take final finishing.

One-shot volunteers are still busy. Working from the sheer down to the keel with their plywood scrapers, all the mortar that is proud of the mesh on the interior is scraped down into the keel where it is re-bucketed out of the boat, taken away

30 Is that what they call floating cement? Note walkway to enable the plasterers to reach all parts of the hull easily.

31 The scraped and broomed interior of *Spray* immediately after the
last volunteer climbed out of the hull.

and dumped; not left where it might get inadvertently re-
used. The scraping, which will have revealed the bare metal
of the mesh, is followed by brushing which recoats the steel
with a thin layer of cement; stiff brooms or handbrushes of
the kind you might use for stubborn dirt on a carpet are ideal.
A neat, not unattractive mesh-patterned finish now emerges
and it is worth spending an extra half-hour putting the final
touches to it. The builder and a knowledgeable friend should
take time, when the other volunteers have left the hull, to do
that little extra brushing in corners and along web-frames
that really finishes the job. When you are really satisfied, cut
away the limber hole blanks, leave the hull and issue the
solemn edict that no one—*but no one*—goes back inside.

So now everyone sits around, talking big seas or motorway
contracts, eating doughnuts, drinking coffee and the builder,
with slyly romantic looks at his new boat, gets his breath.
This is where you find out whether the mix was too wet: wet
mixes take forever to go off. One builder I know was driven

to dismembering the hot-dog fire in the hope that smoking branches would dry the hull surface faster: some thought it was a new kipper-style curing system. Of course, the weather has a lot of effect here: cold, damp, wind-less days being the worst. If it's photographer's sailing weather, there will be little time to natter.

When the plasterers give the word, the mixer is re-started though this time it may only make one or two batches. Using the derbies, the whole hull is rodded off, removing high spots and filling in hollows with the fresh mix though never repairing defects in your meshing with lots of cement. You have already asked for a coat of $\frac{1}{8}$-inch thick maximum and ex-

32   This is the skilled stuff. Plasterer Dougie Patterson of Porthleven using a 'derby' on *Spray*.

plained carefully that you would prefer a buoyant bumpy boat to a smooth-skinned sculpture.

Then comes the final finish. Different teams seem to have their own ideas as to how it is achieved but the best ones always take an age over it. Some use steel floats, some prefer small wood floats, some may go then to sponges or back to steel floats. You'll have gathered some idea of the finish you want when you looked at the other fellows' boats and will have already talked to the plasterers about it. It sounds odd to say that you may not have asked for the smoothest possible finish (meaning steel floats). Read Bruce Bingham and you will learn that too good a finish can mean problems of paint adhesion later, requiring etching acids and the like. You may opt for the slightly rougher sponge finish, as many have done locally, to make painting her easy.

Depending on boat size, the weather and other factors, it may be well into the afternoon before the last volunteer has gone home: even when everyone works hard, there is always one volunteer who works hardest and stays longest: in our case, it was Brian Williamson who also took some of the better photographs in this book. The plasterers clean off their trowels diplomatically as your wife dips into her handbag: plasterers do like cash and eventually you are left to look at the boat you have built.

There is a temptation to relax at this stage, pat yourself on the back and contemplate the hot bath ahead. I'm sorry you can't—yet. Now is the time to get the hull shrouded in polythene and tarps in as windtight a manner as possible but making sure that you don't even touch the setting hull surface. The purpose is to put off starting the water cure as long as possible: start the water cure too early and at best your hull will show the runs, at worst great flakes of soft mortar will fall away. Unfortunately, different parts of the hull will dry out at different rates and you may find curing water seems needed in one region while others are too soft to allow it. The answer is localized wetting with a damp sponge or stirrup pump. Thus you may spend the rest of the day coming back at two-hourly intervals to damp down as needed. If it's raining, you may not start the water cure until the following morning but it's more likely that when your volunteers are responding to the call for 'Last Orders', you'll be turning on the curing system. Let's hope it works.

Wake up betimes next morning. If it's raining, you can go back to sleep; if it's one of those magic summer mornings where the sun is up by six and hot by seven, you have just got to go and look at the boat. What you are hoping not to find are thin streaks of paler mortar indicating blocked holes in the hose above. Sure, they can be opened again with a length of wire but there is more to life than hole jabbing.

33 The start of the cure. Note hose wire-tied to sheer batten and rough timber frame higher up to which polythene will be stapled.

When you are sure everything is running, get out a collection of thin cotton rags and drape them over the curing hose, smoothing the wet cloth against the hull so that it 'sticks' there, diffusing the individual jets of water so that a thin wet curtain runs uniformly down the hull surface.

There are always teething troubles with such systems, it seems, and you can expect to spend much of the second day down by the boat, just ensuring that all is running as it should. A useful occupation, if you have any energy left at all, is to rub any sand off the surface of the hull. Naturally you would not use grinding gear at this stage, the hull is far too green to take it but any local rough spots can be cleaned up considerably simply by rubbing gently with a softwood block. By the end of the second day, your little craft will look a whole lot nicer, she will be curing steadily and you will be looking forward to getting back to work on Monday morning, just to catch up on some rest.

Five days later and you can walk safely on the cement, two weeks later and two-shotters start to plaster their interiors. Luc Delahaie organized half a dozen volunteers and without professional plasterers, did the whole of the interior of his 38-footer in a weekend. Derek and Sue Blundell, with their massive Hartley 45, arranged things so that he plastered while she mixed and with no other help, they produced an incredibly neat interior working at the rate of two or three hull sections each day. Obviously, with the smaller hull I'm hoping you'll choose for your first ferro boat, you'll manage in far less time. Whether you employ a plasterer to put on the final finish or attempt it yourself depends on your purse and your confidence. Certainly, the amateurs who did it themselves seem to have achieved satisfactory results by working slowly and carefully, deliberately avoiding any sort of 'Go—Go—Go!' atmosphere. Working from the keel upwards, floating mortar inward and upward against the freshly grouted skin, the only area of difficulty seems to be a hard

34 Interior of Luc Delahaie's double-ender after two-shot plastering
of the interior. Note battens to support hull between frames. (This
photograph was taken after the cement had cured and the
wire loops had been removed.)

turn of the bilge where a build up of extra cement is possible
on the inside of the concave curve. One way around this and
any doubts you may have about your plastering ability,
would be to adopt a Benford scrape-and-brush finish on the
interior of a two-shot hull, with the extra weight saved as a
further bonus.

A fortnight on, and two-shotters (plus the one-shotters who
did not do all the hull), may tackle the underside of the decks.
The only preparation is the wiring of lots of fore and aft
battens to the topside of the deck to take the cement load and
keep everything fair. Again whether you employ a plasterer
or two is optional but whatever you do, if mud-pushing volunteers will be needed, get plenty. Pushing cement into mesh

Halifax -
Biggest Building society in
the World   HALIFAX

FISHER NAUTICAL
157 SACKVILLE ROAD
   HOVE
        SUSSEX BN3 3HD

      Tel. 0273 721111

overhead, with no really good flat surface to brace your feet on, is hard work indeed. Hardest of all, as you would expect, is a pointed fore-peak and a tapering counter. Start at the ends first and work amidships. You'll find that floats are more useful pushing mud upward but the effort needed is greater, especially since you may have to push the mortar over half-way to persuade it to stay there. Finish the underside, smooth or brushed, and rearrange the curing hose: you'll find that the exposed mesh on the top face of the deck holds water well so ensuring a good cure. However, the underside is a different story: however good your jets, you will probably have to slip inside frequently to spray the inevitable patches which seem to dry in no time.

Last of all comes the top surface of the deck and this time it is probably as well to have the plasterers back to do the

35 Luc Delahaie's preparations for plastering the underside of the
deck: stiffening battens usually run for and aft,
but Luc has his own ideas!

36 Even when deck plastering, adequate protection against wind and sun is essential.

final finish for, with its relatively flat surface, any errors in deck fairness will really stand out. On our own boat, plasterers Jackie Harris and Doug Patterson of Porthleven adopted the technique of first floating on a very thin coat of mortar so wet as to be grout almost. When this had had a chance to seep in and around the mesh and into any voids in between hull and deck, they applied a very stiff mix indeed, almost like damp sand, which was really worked hard down into the grout of the top surface. Finally, with lots of checks to see that the top coat of mortar was as thin as possible, the

37 Block and tackle system
in use to take cement to the
plasterers doing the
underside of the deck.

38 Mortar coming through
from the underside. Note
better penetration required
in deck/house angle at
this stage and use of portlight
as hole 'blank'.

surface was floated and sponged. It was not a long job and I'm sure that most 30-footers could be finished in a morning: ours, with the added fiddle of coachroof sides and bulwarks, still left us time to watch the Cup Final on the box.

When this cure is complete, you can take down your hose for sale to the ferro builder down the road, remove tarps and polythene and any timber battens still left across the web frames. Similarly, with hacksaw and cold chisel, you can attack the LWL pipes between the frames, the centreline pipe and so on. Then get the advice of a boatbuilder or knowledgeable amateur and shore up the hull really well, taking care to ensure that when you cut away the web frame extensions by which she has hung until plastering, not only does she not fall over (!) but that she does not move at all. Then you will be able to continue using your spirit level throughout the fitting out.

There is still one last plastering session. There are lots of unsightly holes and patches of mesh where there were bars, battens, limber hole blanks and, of course, the stern tube region. Now is the time to locate the tube carefully using wires and plywood shuttering to hold it firmly in place while mortar is put in around it. You may decide to cast the tube in permanently with provision for replacing worn bearings, or use a system which allows the tube's removal either by casting in a steel pipe to enclose the stern tube permanently, or a plastic pipe to act as a removable pattern. Alignment is everything and must be taken carefully: one fishing boatbuilder I know did everything by sighting through the tube to a mark on the inside of the stem.

When all is in place and ready, you can start on the last plastering day. As long as there is one volunteer to make up small batches of mix, you will be able to cope alone with priming the existing surfaces with concrete adhesive and then cementing in all the various imperfections, starting with the stern tube surround. Here we found that a length of stringer

39 After the cure. The author's *Spray* after the scaffolding came
down. In the heel note pegs for pintle holes, bare mesh at the end of
the stern-tube nacelle and drain for curing water.

rod chucked into an electric drill made a reasonably gentle vibrator to get mortar down below the tube. Curing of all these areas is not difficult with the rest of the hull offering protection from the wind: cloth and sacking wetted daily will suffice.

12

Any year now

Here I am nearing the end of my book and your boat is no more than a quarter finished. However, from here on you are in the relatively established territory of fitting out any sort of hull and the fact that your hull is made of cement has less and less special relevance as work goes ahead. Obviously, there is a wide range of standards of finish and general excellence to which you can finish her, depending on your ability, your pocket and, most of all, your time. Down the middle of the road, Richard Hartley's book gives some excellent instruction on how the more modern looking ferrocement boat might be furnished and finished without too great an outlay, and providing motive power for such a craft, Nigel Warren's book *Marine Conversions* (Adlard Coles Ltd) is a useful guide to the modification of car and lorry engines. For those who want a real yacht of high quality, Robert Tucker's *Fitting Out Ferrocement Hulls* (Adlard Coles Ltd) is an equally invaluable guide. However, at the simple, homely and economical end of the scale, the fitter-out of the small ferro boat is still feeling his way to some extent and much depends on the choice of design, the best giving an immense amount of detailed advice to those who, through poverty or a simple desire to be able to fix it when it breaks, want to make as much themselves as possible.

Let me start you off, then, with one or two suggestions.

When it comes to filling any hollows and painting the hull, most methods tend to be expensive, I'm afraid. This is because not any old filler or any old paint will stick to cement and stay stuck. Trial and error over the years by many seems to indicate that the best fillers for ferrocement are epoxy-based, and that paints should be either epoxies or chlorinated rubber. Thus one can now buy prettily packaged epoxy fillers and epoxy paint 'for yachts' or, at least, you can buy them if you can afford them. On the other hand, you can save some money and still do a reasonable job by buying the epoxy repair kits sold for concrete pipes or better still, buying epoxy resin from firms like Strand Glass Ltd and industrial talcum powder to make up a filler of your own. Experiments will show which proportion of goo to talc works best: we found something like a 50/50 by volume worked well, though hot days meant more powder.

When you come to paint the hull, at least a couple of months after the last cure, you can make considerable savings if you are prepared to struggle on without a yacht or ship's wheel on your paint tin. For example, Berger Chemicals, Sealocrete and Polybond all make pitch- or coal-tar-based epoxy paints which have been used successfully on ferro-cement; Sealocrete even producing a leaflet as a guide to this use. Also, on both internal and external hull surfaces, we and others have had success with the use of the new water-based epoxy emulsions now appearing on the industrial paints market. We were specially pleased with Sealocrete's 'Epoxy Wetcote' which can be applied to damp cement if need be, requires only water for thinning and brush cleaning, and dries with a pleasing semi-matt finish which looks just right on a glorified workboat. Similarly, we have heard excellent reports of Polybond's 'Q.19' and 'Sansol' epoxy emulsions; though originally developed for industrial and agricultural applications, 'Sansol' has survived six months on a boat in Arctic waters without any trouble at all.

The other surfaces on the boat can also be painted per-fectly well without paying the toll at the chandler's door. In that delightful source of woodenboat wisdom, *Skiffs and Schooners*, Pete Culler makes out an excellent case for the use of domestic exterior paints on the timber of traditional boats and you have probably heard already that exterior wall coatings like 'Sandtex' which contain mica, are a very much cheaper alternative to non-slip deck paints. On galvanized steel work, 'Rotarista' paint is both cheap and good and, what's more, smells like paint used to smell and since that's yet another Sealocrete product, I had better disclaim any connection with them—or any other firms mentioned—here and now!

When it comes to timber for fitting out, for me there are two alternatives: buy in bulk or buy second-hand. Buying new, a bulk order (perhaps by combining with friends) of a log of iroko or larch, sawn 'through and through' longitudinally at some standard thickness that can be used by all, will attract a healthy discount from timber firms like Barchards of Hull, Henry Brownes of Luton or W. W. Howard of Southampton. If you all hire a self-drive truck to go and collect the stuff you save even more.

Second-hand timber is best bought directly from the demolition contractor before some canny middleman has stepped in to take out the nails and put up the price. I know of one 25-foot ferro fishing boat that was fitted out completely in teak, no less, all from 6 by 2 beams bought at £1 per foot from a demolished sevententh-century barn! In no way a parallel coup, at the moment I'm about to start saloon panelling with strips of maple sawn up from tongued and grooved flooring from a hospital physiotherapy unit. In my case, this will all be glued to a job lot of builders' ply which forms bulkheads, etc. Others I know, after facing web frames with timber, have used solid tongued and grooved floorboarding for bulkheads, etc., saving the hassle of manhandling huge chunks of ply into the boat and by using smaller components, making later modifications that much easier.

I've already mentioned Nigel Warren's book as a source of advice on conversions of high-revving modern engines but the ancillaries and the appropriate gearboxes for such conversions are often expensive. Mechanical dunderheads like myself might share my affection for the old type of massively built one-lunged slow-turning thumper which used to push boats about. Modern varieties, like the little Volvos and the beautiful Sabbs, might be beyond your pocket but the second-hand columns of the local paper might produce little Kelvins, Listers or 'Handy-Billies'. You may even find, joy of joys, a defunct old boat with a hull beyond redemption: a source not only of old-style marine engines (they outlast the hull every time) but also tanks and seacocks and even good marine hardware like traditional vents and ports which today cost a bomb. One such sally into boatbreaking obtained us a lovely single-cylinder Lister from a £100 write-off, several other goodies and then, though I blush to admit it, we sold the somewhat ventilated hull for £50. The wheeler-dealing went even further when we decided that our 11-tonner was too much, even for a Lister, so we sold the engine for £75. We are now looking for a wreck with the three-cylinder model!

I have already flogged the virtues of the traditional rig in Chapter 3. Large spars can be hacked out of trees from the Forestry Commission and smaller ones shaped, glued up if need be, from clear-grained fir or spruce if you can get it. By this stage, you may have gathered enough confidence with your welding gear to make lots of the necessary fittings in mild steel, sending them along for hot-dip galvanizing before installation. Like me, you may even find a local blacksmith able to work eyes into the ends of your chainplates so that you can use deadeyes which you can make yourself in ash or oak or have them turned up in a metal working lathe if you can get the traditional lignum vitae. Fishermen's suppliers are good sources of all sorts of rope, rigging wire and other items, I'm told, though I have not got to that stage myself. Whether you go the whole hog and make your own sails depends on your confidence, I suppose: new, second-hand or home-made, if they are your main source of motive power, make sure that they are good.

These then are just a few random suggestions to set you on your way. I think that you will soon develop a nose for such things yourself as the fitting out gains momentum. You may even get to the stage of turning down something you can easily afford, just for the satisfaction of doing it yourself. By then, though, there are three notes of caution to be sounded. The first is that however competent you become at adapting this and renovating that, some items will be beyond your ability. If it's important and you cannot do it well enough to trust your family's lives to it, forget it, swallow your pride and go see the chandler. The second caution is that doing everything yourself takes for ever. You can spend a day on a dead-eye and a couple of weeks on a companion; you can spend hours searching the district for some mouldy piece of second-hand junk that might needs months of restoration. Is it worth it?

Worst of all is the reaction of those around you to this crawling pace. Once it was rather fun for them to know someone actually building a boat from cement but, from the day you plastered, they have been expecting you to launch. Where once you were an amiable eccentric in their eyes, worth knowing as a novelty, a source of social identity and witty tales of wire twisting, now your apparent slowness over fitting out becomes first an embarrassment and then almost an annoyance. Eventually, they stop asking 'When are you going to launch her?' and begin to sneer 'You'll never get that boat in the water.' As if they ever built anything. You will.

Let me give you some idea . . .

Appendix A
Isn't she lovely . . .?
IOTA

Perhaps more than any other boat mentioned here, *Iota* captures the spirit of this book. (It features on the front cover.) In no way cheap or nasty or botched looking, she was built for a very, very small financial outlay because her builders, Sonny and Kathy Wieck of Seattle, had adopted a simple life-style which left no room for extravagant spending. However, by choosing a boat only 18 feet long, they could afford to build her properly and by selecting a Jay Benford design, they had the benefit of lots of guidance for making many items of the boat's gear themselves.

Iota has berths for two, a proper marine loo and a 'galley' and there is still room enough in the cockpit for comfortable day sailing. Jay Benford has peaked up that gaff nicely and those three booms and the jib furling gear must make for easy handling. She looks simple and effective. Just like the water system on *Serena*, another of the class built by Bill Babcock. He used a traditional cooper-made keg on deck and installed a gravity feed to the bowl in the galley. Pull the plug and it drains into the marine loo. Of course, the keg is small enough to be taken ashore for refilling.

The Wiecks bought their plans in June, 1972, and immediately discovered an advantage of a hull this small: it can be built indoors. They moved themselves into a barn and started work from a Benford pipe-frame kit, saving not only pipe-bending problems but the lofting stage also. Photographs of the meshed hull show the time and care that must have gone

40 Sonny and Kathy Wieck's 18-foot 'Canoe Yawl' *Iota*.

into producing an exceptionally fair armature and also show
the filigree beauty of a well-made ferro basket. The armature
was plastered in the 80°F of a Seattle high summer using a
US Type Three cement (high strength, early setting). With
the protection of the shed, the combination of a high ambient
temperature and a water cure, the resultant steam bath had

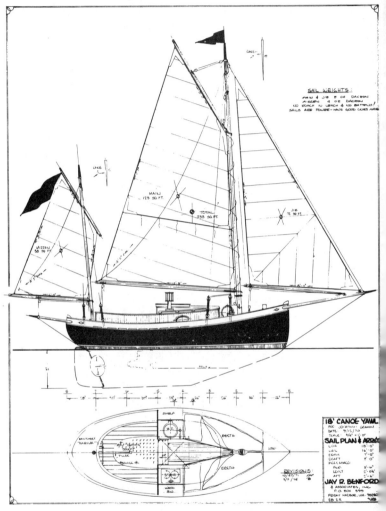

Fig 21 An 18-foot 'Canoe yawl' by Jay R. Benford.

the compressive strength of the hull up to 9,400 psi in just seven days and the cure was concluded then. (But this type of cement sets too quickly for use on much larger boats.) The finished hull was just $\frac{1}{2}$ inch thick.

Sonny Wieck has the patience and imagination to find new uses for what his affluent American neighbours see as garbage. It would take a life-time of 'scrounging' to fit out the average 40-footer but when your ship is 18 feet small, off-cuts and the occasional bargain can go a long way. *Iota*'s attractive house and cockpit area were all built from the thrown-away timber of local manufacturing industries. Down below, berth cushions too were home-made, stuffed with scraps of upholstery cushions and foam pieces which were once carpet backing. The loo is a rubber pail, a seventies sophistication of the immortal Herreshoff cedar-wood chuck-it-bucket and the wood-burning stove, for heating and cooking, was made up by Sonny from discarded iron plate and is efficient enough for Kathy to bake bread. Sonny went on scrounging: a couple of ports from a beached hulk, free for the asking, two brass bilge pumps freed and working, trolling poles for masts and nylon rope from fishermen's dumps . . . and so on. Four years from the start, *Iota* was launched.

With little previous cruising experience—Kathy says 'She knew far more about sailing than we did'—the Wiecks took time to get to know their little boat in the waters of Puget Sound and around the San Juan Islands. They found her stable, responsive and buoyant, easy to push and a good boat to learn with. Then, in the summer of 1975, they set out on a testing trip up the west coast of the USA and Canada to Steamboat Bay, Ketchikan, Alaska, using a British Seagull outboard as sole auxiliary power. Here they have lived and sailed until, at the time of writing, they are starting on their return journey to the sunnier waters of the Puget Sound.

Every boat owner has a regret or two: Sonny and Kathy now wish that they had fitted an inboard 7-HP diesel from the start: the outboard can push at 5 knots in a calm but isn't really up to pushing *Iota* home against a wind and a 4-foot 'chop'. Similarly, they would have gone for cement decks instead of ply and, if it had been available at the time, maybe the 23-foot version of the canoe yawl with over 6 feet of headroom. Still, on reflection, they think that building a boat as small as *Iota* was a wise decision because learning the techniques of fitting out even a small boat properly, and doing a job well, takes time. Doing it this way, they feel they got 'a fine little ship' and they got her sailing.

STAN'S WORKING BOAT

Here at Falmouth, in Cornwall, 'a working boat' is not a general term, it is the local name for the craft of the last commercial sailing fleet in Europe. They are typical Victorian gaff cutters with straight stems and plumb transoms: 'yachty' ends are wasteful and these boats have a living to earn. There are two basic sizes with a few mongrels in between: the two-man boats tow two oyster dredges across the banks of Carrick Roads and they are 28 feet long, and there is a smaller group of craft around 22 feet overall.

In winter, size dictates how many dredges you work; in summer, it decides which class you enter for the Saturday village regattas. Working boat races are working men's sport, nearer in spirit and spectacle to the fishing smack and barge matches of the last century than the parades of pampered plastic which are today's yacht races.

For these races, the boats sprout Cornish yard topsails, with the heel of the pole fitted with a 'timanoggy' reeving through a bulls-eye on the inboard end of the gaff, giving the topsail its characteristic forward rake. The efficiency of this rig—not only running and reaching—has surprised more than one Bermudan-slooped yachtsman as he was left behind in an alcoholic slipstream.

174

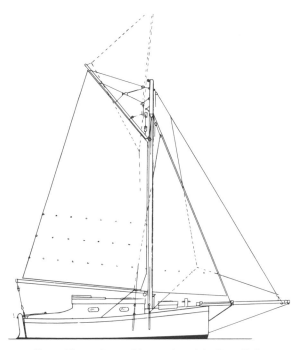

Fig 22 The 22-foot cruising version of the Percy Dalton 'Falmouth Working Boat'.

41 Stan's working boat being fitted out for the 1977 season.

Stan Goldman, a Falmouth engineer, had his first experience of ferrocement boatbuilding with the 50-foot squaresail ketch *Hardiesse*, designed by Percy Dalton for the local Sea Scouts. There was some steel and mesh left over so Stan went back to Percy, who had already designed working boats for local fishermen for wood, resinglass and 'C-Flex' construction, and asked for the lines and offsets for a 22-footer to be built in cement. Percy was happy to oblige, attempting to combine the best qualities of existing working boats in a design which would lend itself to easy conversion to a cruising yacht.

With the racing season approaching, time was tight and Stan was able to draw on his previous ferro experience in order to cut corners. He dispensed with the usual building frame and bent up frames from $\frac{3}{8}$-inch mild steel rod which were welded to the keel, previously set up on blocks. Stem, transom and floors were added in the same material and $\frac{3}{8}$-inch bar was welded to each frame as the sheerline. For stringers, Stan bought two coils of $\frac{1}{8}$-inch high tensile fencing wire and attaching one end to the stem, simply walked around the boat, unwinding as he went. An assistant followed with spring steel wire clips to attach the continuous stringer to each frame. Fairing was not even attempted until two layers of $\frac{1}{2}$-inch 19-gauge square welded mesh were attached inside and out and the whole thing wire-tied at two-inch centres.

Stan estimates that building time, up to plastering day, was around 90 hours. Two local plasterers were employed, using a 1:1:1 mix of ordinary Portland cement and Blue Elvan and Blackpool (in Cornwall!) sands and the finished hull was around $\frac{3}{8}$-inch thick. She required approximately $1\frac{1}{2}$ tons of scrap steel and cement ballast to bring her to her marks. Spars were grown sticks and all ironwork was homemade. Sails were borrowed from other working boats and in a flurry of last-minute jobs, unnamed and hardly finished, she was racing.

It is Stan's regret that more time was not available to bring her to a higher standard of finish and he looks forward to building a more refined successor at his new home in Canada, perhaps a 28-footer this time, like the two already in frame here in Cornwall.

Not that the record of the little anonymous first one is all that bad: in its class, the little cement boat has had three firsts (one of these in very light winds), two seconds and several thirds. Indeed, on the day she won the St Mawes 'Victory Cup', in near gale conditions, the cement boat kept going when all the rest retired. She went so fast, the helmsman claimed, he could see the boat's own wave cresting a yard behind her transom!

SIMPLICITY

Now where on earth do I start to describe this one? *Simplicity* is our as yet unlaunched version of Joshua Slocum's *Spray* and quite a welter of unconnected details of her construction have already been inflicted on you. Could you stand a summary . . .?

Basically, I drew out a five-sixths version of the lines of the old sloop, increased the draught back to that of the original, added more freeboard and a limey's attempt at an American schooner stern. Percy Dalton then had all this scribble dumped upon his drawing board with the request to make it all into a boat. Somehow, he succeeded handsomely and the finished hull is 33 feet long on deck, nearly 12 feet wide and draws around 4 feet at the heel; to Maggie and I a cheerful, homely tub of a boat that recalls Essex bawleys and Cornish barges and still has much about her of the old boat that crossed the world's oceans. If we have managed to retain it, the *Spray* hull's aversion to constant helm tending would suit me fine, but both the original rigs featured too large a mainsail for our liking. Thus we've substituted a sort

42 Maggie at work on *Simplicity*, our adaptation of Slocum's *Spray*.

of pre-1840 or Oland Islands style of schooner rig with a largish foresail and relatively small main, hoping to reduce individual sails to handleable proportions and yet maintain a healthy sail area and—most important—the long-based rig which was half the secret of the *Spray*'s self-steering ability.

However, Percy Dalton carries none of the responsibility for the constructional techniques: these are of my own devising, most shamelessly cribbed from other ferro boats with some similar characteristics. Thus she has web frames at 30-inch centres, each with a deep floor up to sole level, stringers of hard-drawn rod at 2-inch centres, two layers of welded mesh and one layer of diagonal chicken netting outside and four layers of chicken netting inside. Subsequent experience has persuaded me that another similar boat would have an all-welded mesh lay-up, with perhaps chicken netting for low coamings and web frames. This was the lay-up used on *Simplicity*'s ferro deck and house sides. She also has ferro-

178

cement bulwarks 14 inches high and, again, this is something I would change on Mark Two: the meshing and plastering of the bulwarks was all too time-consuming and fiddly; another time they would be made of wood.

Frames were built at a leisurely pace over the evenings of the winter of 1974–5 and in April, we set up our scaffolding in the little boatyard by Penryn Bridge, where everyone has been so extraordinarily kind and helpful to us. Plastering day, appropriately, was around 1 April 1976, when the hull was cemented by the Benford system, with the enthusiastic assistance of boatbuilding students from Falmouth Technical College. Decks and house were done on the Hartley system and the final cure was finished by the end of May.

Fig 23 Percy Dalton's impression of *Simplicity*, as we hope she'll be.

Since then until the time of writing, summer '77, we have been fitting out slowly and somewhat spasmodically, as finances fluctuate.

The first job was the lid of the coachroof which consists of two layers of 9-mm ply over laminated larch beams. This in turn was covered with woven glass cloth laid in polyester resin. Bowsprit bitts in oak, hatches in ply and larch and a square removable skylight fabricated from the mahogany doors of a redundant minesweeper all followed. Ports from a defunct motor boat were cleaned up and fitted and, inside, *Simplicity* now has floor beams, a fitted-out forepeak and a gypsy caravan-type coal stove which connects to a home-made coaster-style T-shaped smoke head. In fact, she is so dry and weather-tight that, rather than attempt to write this book aboard the converted Hastings lugger which is our temporary summer home, it seemed an obvious move to bring an old table into what will one day be a spacious saloon, set up my typewriter and work right here; I can vouch that in addition to its other virtues, ferrocement muffles outside noises very effectively, which has done wonders for my some-what erratic concentration.

As I have mentioned earlier, my next task—in about four thousand words' time—will be to finish the saloon furnishings with exterior grade ply and then panel it with maple. I also have the iroko I need to finish the companion hatch which has stood half-completed through the summer months. Simultaneously, since I never seem able to do one job at once, there are two substantial beltings (all right, yotters, rubbing strakes) to be bolted on, and the hull to be painted. Hopefully, sometime in the winter of '77–'78, we will find and install the ridiculously cheap 20-HP air-cooled diesel we have been seeking for some months now and, all being well, *Simplicity* might be afloat, still unrigged and only part furnished, in the spring of '78; three years after first setting up the frames.

THE LIVEABOARDS

Nowadays, it seems that every harbour has its liveaboards: people whose boats are their homes, winter and summer alike, and who soon must amass more experience of the joys and problems of living comfortably on a boat than most of us can gather in a life-time of week-ends and holidays. Not all are seasoned world voyagers though, few are rich and fewer still are hippy dropouts. Most in fact are everyday folk who have chosen an alternative to the flat, cottage or semi. Derek and Sue Blundell are not yet afloat but their boat reflects so much care and thought that it is already interesting.

When I visited Derek and Sue on their superb Hartley 'Tahitian', it was only a month after their arrival at the tiny shipyard at Porthleven in West Cornwall. They had arrived, not by sea but by low-loader from a builder's yard near Helston, where they built their 45-foot bilge keeler. The idea of building their own boat had come quietly enough when they were out-bid on a piece of land on which they had hoped to build their own house. Since then, both have worked equally and tremendously hard, taking it in turns to earn a living while the other works on the boat. Six months earlier, with the forward part of the boat complete, they were able to move aboard and concentrate on finishing the centre cockpit and after cabin.

'We chose ferrocement', Derek told me, 'because it seemed the only material which did not demand too many specialized techniques or too much initial expense.' Like all Richard Hartley designs, the hull is built around web frames and a chicken netting armature and plastered by the two-shot Sayers system. The Blundells commended the Hartley plans as both comprehensible and complete and explained that they were particularly attracted by the spacious and comfortable lay-out of the 'Tahitian' which would allow them

43 & 44 Derek and Sue Blundell's comfortable Hartley 'Tahitian'
with interior fitting-out well advanced.

to carry charter passengers on their wanderings to the Med.
and beyond. The present accommodation includes a V-bunk
cabin in the bows, another two-berth cabin aft of the shower/
loo compartment on the starboard side and to port a diesel
heater and well-equipped galley. Aft of this comes the chart-

table and opposite, a comfortable dinette. Throughout the accommodation, much of the cement has been hidden by sapele-faced ply, clear varnished to match the laminated pine coachroof beams, utile furniture and hardwood louvre doors. The outside of the hull was filled with Piridite, an industrial epoxy concrete filler and painted with Epilux epoxies from Bergers.

Both agreed that even on land, they derived much satisfaction from being independent of mains services. Here Derek's experience as a plumber has helped him build in many useful features. In particular, they have not only extensive fresh water capacity under the sole but also a used-water tank (into which flows water from washing, showers, etc.) and this is used to flush the loo into a further holding tank. Another refinement is the pressure accumulator in the cold water system, simply a 3-foot length of plastic soil pipe inserted vertically in the piping system where a 24-volt pump can create an air buffer which gives domestic type water-flow. To save on heat wastage, conventional hot water pipe has been replaced by 10-mm semi-insulated microbore central heating tube: it's not only cheaper, it's easier to bend around a boat's curves. The foot tray in the shower is also evidence of Derek's ingenuity: instead of a conventional model costing pounds, he cut the bottom six inches from a fibreglass water cistern and used the rest of tank sides to make four-inch tiles to finish the loo floor. An 85-HP Perkins diesel has been installed together with a small Lister to provide the 'juice' for a built-in washing machine, deep freeze and other electrical appliances. Next comes the sloop rig: over 1,000 square feet of sail and a 52-foot mast. Here Derek has a small regret: 'I think if I were building again I would opt for a traditional rig,' he said. 'Then I could make far more of my own fittings instead of paying the staggering prices of modern equipment for a boat of this size.'

GALOWA

After fifteen years as a merchant seaman, Mike Robson left his job as a bosun to come ashore. But not for long: a week in a factory was sufficient to convince him he was not cut out for land-life and so, having spent many a 'shore-leave' taking out charter parties in his 30-foot ketch-rigged lifeboat conversion, he decided that a larger boat, specially designed for the job, would give him a home, a new career and a satisfying way of life. Thus, after accruing some capital on a Scottish tunnel-digging project, he took a job working nights down a Yorkshire coal mine and built his boat during the day.

The design Mike chose was Samson Marine's 54-foot wishbone schooner 'C-Lord': a classic clipper-bowed dreamship, the plans of which he found complete and easy to follow. With such a large boat, hull weights are less critical and to save money he chose 'traditional' ferrocement construction techniques. Thus the frames are waterpipe (when I asked if he had any trouble bending them to shape, Mike looked puzzled and then said 'No, I just bent them by hand around my knee!') and the mesh is chicken netting throughout. The armature was completed, decks and all, in just four months, and a gang of thirty plastered her in one go.

The next four years were dedicated exclusively to the mammoth task of fitting her out single-handed, living in a caravan on the boatbuilding site and still working each night down the pit. Not only was there the woodwork of three double cabins for charter parties, bosun's store, galley, dining area, shower, etc., there was also a large semi-raised main saloon which he not only panelled himself but also provided with a professional looking upholstered L-shaped settee. Outside, there was an imitation laid deck of iroko, massive homemade cleats and blocks and even the making of three ships' wheels: the first two went to friends. On the mechanical side, Mike converted a Perkins engine from a combine Harvester,

45　Mike Robson's tremendous single-handed boatbuilding achievement: the 54-foot wishbone schooner *Galowa*.

made his own anchors and even the winches to hoist them
from bus door-closing motors.

Finally, she was launched into a West Riding canal, busy
with barge traffic, and motored to the little port of Goole to
be rigged. The masts were two 50-foot spruces that Mike had

felled and shaped himself and the bowsprit came out of an enormous baulk of pitch-pine with the help of a chain saw. The masts are stayed with galvanized wire rope and industrial iron rigging screws and the mast-tracks are substantial galvanized section from an electrical conduit suppliers in which run home-made Tufnol slides. The exceptionally free-running headsail furling gears were fabricated from car wheel hubs and the spreader lights came from sealed beam headlamps, suitably encased. All the sails are of canvas and the panels were cut and tacked together by Mike before being sent away to have seams sewn professionally.

Christened *Galowa* after the miners' name for a pit pony, Mike's boat left Goole four years after he started building her, for the East Coast resort of Whitby where he spent the season on daily and weekly charters. The parties rarely included even amateur sailors and so it was essential that *Galowa* should function happily as a single-hander. Mike believes that in this respect her size is an asset since the massive hull provides a firm, stable and predictable platform on which to work. However, just as valuable to the single-hander is the wishbone schooner rig which reduces the areas of all sails to controllable dimensions and makes all but the jib self-tending.

Now chartering from Shipshape, St Mawes, in Cornwall, Mike has plans which include eventual charters further afield in warmer climes, and then another boat, larger yet at around 70 feet. She too will be ferrocement: hull, decks, even coachroof. Mike says that after two seasons working *Galowa* hard, he is more convinced than ever that as a boatbuilding material, ferrocement is 'right'.

L.01 8587211

Marston Book Services.

5832412

Appendix B
Bibliography, Useful addresses

The following list of books and addresses is by no means exhaustive and will not always be up to date, of course. In case of difficulty, try a current issue of one of the more practical boating magazines for up to date sources.

Further reading:

Practical Ferrocement Boatbuilding, Jay R. Benford & Herman Husen, International Marine Publishing Co., Camden, Me 04843, USA.

Hartley's Ferrocement Boatbuilding, R. Hartley & A. J. Reid, Boughtwood Printing House, c/o Richard Hartley, Box 30094, Takapuna North, Auckland, New Zealand. (Both of these very highly recommended.)

Ferrocement: Design, Techniques & Application, Bruce Bingham, Cornell Maritime Press, Cambridge, Md 21613, USA.

Box Po 456 CENTIVIC Maryland 21617 U.S.A.

Ferrocement Yacht Construction, Chris Cairncross, Adlard Coles Ltd, Frogmore, St Albans, Herts.

F.A.O. Investigates Ferrocement Fishing Craft, Fishing News Books Ltd, 23 Rosemont Ave, West Byfleet, Surrey.

For information on 'ferro-resin' construction:

A Revolution in Ferro Construction, Platt Monfort, Aladdin Products Inc., RFD 2, Wiscasset, Me 04578, USA.

For fitting out information:

Fitting Out Ferrocement Hulls, Robert Tucker, Adlard Coles Ltd, Frogmore, St Albans, Herts.

Marine Conversions, Nigel Warren, Adlard Coles Ltd, Frogmore, St Albans, Herts.

Other sources of information:

The Information Division, Cement & Concrete
  Association, 52 Grosvenor Gardens, London SW1W 0AQ.
International Ferrocement Information Center, PO Box
  2754, Bangkok, Thailand.

Designers and firms selling boat plans:

Richard Hartley, Box 30094, Takapuna North, Auckland,
  New Zealand.
New Zealand Ferrocement Services Ltd, PO Box 15–447,
  Auckland 7, New Zealand.
Robert Tucker, 58 Southbury Road, Enfield, Middlesex
  EN1 1YB.
Percy Dalton, 72 West Street, Penryn, Cornwall.
Ferro-cement Marine Services Ltd, 160 Station Road,
  Burnham-on-Crouch, Essex CM0 8JX.
Jay R. Benford & Assoc. Inc., PO Box 399, Friday
  Harbor, Wash. 98250, USA.

And others . . . :

Potter & Bishop (Ferrocement) Ltd, Westerham Heights,
  Westerham, Kent. Suppliers of plans by Hartley,
  Donovan, Tucker & Bruce Roberts. Also supply frame
  kits, spring clips, Bingham's book, etc.
MacAlister Carvall Ltd, Stem Lane Industrial Estate,
  New Milton, Hampshire BH25 5NN. Plans by Benford,
  suppliers of RF Yacht Mortar and other fitting-out
  products.

188

Other useful addresses:

Spring clips.
   Valmerline Ltd, 50 Marlborough Road, Falmouth,
   Cornwall.

'Str-r-etch' mesh, 'Wire-Plank', etc.
   Aladdin Products Inc., RFD 2, Wiscasset, Me 04578,
   USA.

Curing Aids, Pitch Epoxy Paints, Epoxy Emulsions, etc.
   Sealocrete Group Sales Ltd, Atlantic Works, Oakley
   Road, Southampton so9 4FL.

Epoxy Coaltar Paints, Epoxy Emulsions, etc.
   Polybond Limited, 42/44 Warsash Road, Warsash,
   Southampton so3 6HX.

'Nylafilm' coatings: nylon paints for cement etc.
   Falmouth Plastic Co. Ltd, Penwerris Lane, Falmouth,
   Cornwall.

Books on ferrocement & other marine topics.
   M & P Miller's Nautical Bookshop, Arwenack Street,
   Falmouth, Cornwall.

Index